Terry Sanderson's

A to Z of GAY SEX

An erotic alphabet.

Terry Sanderson's A-Z of Gay Sex
First published by The Other Way Press, PO Box 130, London W5 1DQ.

ISBN: 0 948982 06 3

A catalogue record for this book is available from the British Library

Printed in Great Britain
Cover designed by Mark Varey, Number 20 Design, 20 Hamilton Road, Worcester WR5 1AG
Distributed by Turnaround Distribution, 27 Horsell Road, London N5 1XL
Some of the material in this book has already appeared in HIM Magazine.

Information about other books from the Other Way Press can be obtained by sending a first class stamp to The Other Way Press, PO Box 130, London W5 1DQ.

AUTHOR'S NOTE

"Sexually we are not alike. What turns me on may leave you absolutely cold, your fidelity may be a total impossibility for me, and old X's celibacy may be a mystery to both of us. Sexuality emerges from deep springs in our personalities, the Artesian wells of love and longing to which none of us has the key, and we would do well to be humble in the face of this powerful mystery, and above all not to imagine that what suits us may, or should, suit others. Sexually we come in all shapes and sizes, all of them innocent at first, all of them seeking warmth and affection and closeness, until distorted by shame, fear and greed." – Monica Furlong.

From my days as an agony aunt, receiving up to 200 letters a week, I know that there is a frightening level of ignorance of sexual matters among Britain's heterosexual population. There is little evidence to show that the picture is much different among its homosexuals.

This book aims to challenge this, and some of the "shame, fear and greed" that limits sex for so many gay men.

I've gathered as much information as I can, from a wealth of different sources, and arranged it in a way that I hope will be helpful and entertaining.

But this is by no means an academic treatise. It's meant to be an ideas book. It's supposed to show that sex isn't just a pressing, worrisome nuisance that can become an obsession, but also something that can be fun. Safe. Beautiful. Lustful. Satisfying. Hilarious. Life-enhancing. Loving

You'll find in these pages a bit of biology – the bit they left out at school – some history, geography, anthropology, medicine and social comment. There's a bit of trivia, a lot of vital information, and just a tiny bit of facetiousness so that we don't forget that sex is for pleasure as well as other purposes. By the time you reach the end, I hope you'll know a bit more about your body and a lot more about your sexuality.

Give guilt the heave-ho. Relax. Play hard, but play safely.

While every care has been taken to check groups, organisations and businesses mentioned, we can't guarantee that they'll still be in existence when this book reaches the shops.

Abdomen

The abdomen is that area between the bottom of the rib cage and the top of the pubic area – the wall that holds in most of your vital organs. You will recognise it instantly as the bodily part most likely to behave like a balloon if it is neglected for any length of time. Many gay men take great pains to ensure their stomach stays flat; a taut tummy is an absolute prerequisite of any body-shaping regime. Out-of-control inflation in the abdominal area is a sure sign that our youth, so valued by the community, is a thing of the past. Either that or you've eaten too many Mars bars or drunk too many Red Stripes.

But try as we may, when middle-age approaches, it becomes an increasingly debilitating battle to keep that belly under control. Efforts are often undermined by the irresistible force of gravity which pulls outwards and downwards in a most invidious manner. An exercise regime might help you preserve the coveted flat tummy for a while (indeed, there are hundreds of books with titles like 'Have a flat tummy in ten minutes a day' or 'Flatten your stomach without giving up Mars bars').

You can save yourself the trouble and expense of reading these volumes, as most of them can be reduced to a single exercise, as follows: Lie on your back with your hands flat by your side, palms facing down. Pull in your stomach muscles so that your pelvis tilts and your lower back presses into the floor. Bend your knees into your chest and lift your legs up until they are at a right angle to your upper body. Cross your ankles – your knees will naturally move towards your shoulders. Now lower your hips back towards the floor (but not all the way) and repeat the exercise ten to fifteen times. Use your lower stomach muscles rather than the muscles in your lower back, to control the rocking movement. Make sure that you keep your lower back pressed firmly to the floor. Exhale slowly as you lower your legs; then inhale as your raise them.

For all your efforts, you will eventually be overwhelmed by the inevitability of time. At that point the employment of a support garment (known to our mothers as a corset) may be helpful.

Aberration, Abnormality

Gay people are often accused of having 'aberrant' or 'abnormal' sex. But what exactly constitutes 'abnormal' and, indeed, 'normal', in this context? Orthodox religionists have no problem answering this question – whatever *they* do is fine, and whatever anybody else does is an 'abomination'. These moralists tell us that the only acceptable sexual activity is between husband and wife in the missionary position – that is, with the woman on her back and the man on top.

Nobody knows for sure how the missionary position got its name, but the most likely explanation is that it was the position forced on 'primitive' native peoples around the world by Christian missionaries who wanted to spoil everybody's fun.

I once went on holiday to Fiji where, before the arrival of the 19th century Methodist missionaries, sexual abandon was enjoyed by all. When the blue-nosed religious maniacs arrived, however, they clothed the women in long neck-to-ankle dresses and imprisoned the magnificent men in trousers and shirts. The sensuous flaunting in grass skirts was replaced by dreary hymn-singing. This must have been a great loss to the women of Fiji because their men are extremely handsome and most of them well-built with it. But old habits die hard and one imagines that they sang to Jesus in church and worshipped cock the rest of the time. Very much like the home life our own dear gay clergy, in fact.

Agony aunts are inundated with letters from straight people who think they are 'abnormal' because they have sex more than three times a month. These correspondents seem particularly perturbed by oral sex. One woman wrote that she thought oral sex simply meant talking dirty. When she discovered it meant she had to put her husband's dick in her gob she more or less passed out. Gay men, on the other hand, almost universally practise cock-sucking.

There is much less anxiety and fewer hang-ups about 'abnormality' in the gay world and much more willingness to experiment and explore. 'Normality' is a very limiting and tiresome idea. Let uptight straights keep it for themselves.

ACROTOMOPHILIA

This describes someone who is sexually interested in those who have lost a limb (in Greek *acro* means 'extremity', *tomo* means 'cut', and *philia* means 'love').

A study of 183 people who expressed an interest in having sex with an amputee showed that most became aware of their attraction at the time of puberty. Most were of higher intelligence and had achieved well in their occupations. Most also showed no other interest in fetishistic behaviour, and could function well in other sexual situations that didn't involve amputees, so it is difficult to really classify acrotomophilia as a fetish. It is more a 'preference', just as some men like well-built and 'butch' partners, while others prefer the willowy, boyish kind.

However, there is another side to this argument (see Monopodophilia).

Action

Is a euphemism for sex ("how about a bit of action?"). It was used in this sense by Shakespeare in one of his plays, so is not the modern expression so many of us imagine it to be.

Affair

Just what terms can gay men use to describe their relationships? A popular one seems to be 'affair'. This little word covers all eventualities from a full-scale, life-time commitment to any relationship that has lasted more than three days. It might be an affair of the heart or of the arse – whichever, it's very nice.

Affection

The participants in porno films – American ones in particular – seem to exhibit very little affection. It's very much a case of wham-bam-thanks-Uncle-Sam.

But sometimes affection can make all the difference to the way we experience a sexual encounter. Quickie sex-for-its-own-sake has a place, of course, but if it's just a matter of wank, wank, bye-bye, it often leaves us feeling dissatisfied or even cheated. If it has involved a bit of human affection – kissing, cuddling, holding each other close – it is more likely to have been memorable and rewarding. If you are cottaging or trolling in your local wooded rendezvous, it is unlikely that you'll have the time or the inclination for a snogging session, but if you do have the time and privacy, a bit of closeness and intimacy can make all the difference to the encounter. Gay men often complain that they are treated disrespectfully by those who just want a blow-job or whatever and can't even be bothered to give a reassuring squeeze of the arm in gratitude. Once the all-powerful orgasm is achieved, interest evaporates. Perhaps we should make an effort to treat each other better during these casual encounters, making them a little more human in the process. As Dr Bernard Zilbergeld says in his book *Men and Sex*:

"In growing up, girls more than boys were allowed to express and explore their desire for physical contact. Having the permission, girls learned to differentiate their needs for support, comfort, validation and a sense of connection with another, and similar needs, from the need for sex. Boys developed in the opposite direction. Wanting sex was legitimate, even encouraged, while such things as wanting to be held or loved or to know they were not alone were unacceptable...Wanting to hug or to feel close to another sounded too effeminate, but wanting sex was the epitome of masculinity; and in sex you could get some of these other things as well. After years of practice, the man just never felt the need for closeness or comfort or support. All he needed was – sex. Whenever he wanted something that might be called warm or close or loving, he read it as a desire for – sex."

Many men are afraid of the consequences of intimacy and use anonymous sex as a means of getting close to people without making a commitment to knowing that person on a deeper level. Casual sex brings them human contact, but relieves them from the risks of having to expose their vulnerability.

Just because you're over forty doesn't mean your juices have dried up or that your cock has stopped telling you that it wants a bit of attention. However, it's easy to get the idea that the gay scene has an age limit of twenty-five and that if you're over that limit, you aren't welcome. Well, maybe you won't be able to compete on quite the same terms as the disco babes, but it doesn't mean you've stopped wanting sex. Older gay men generally have to find their partners in other places. This is why they are much more attracted to the cottaging and cruising scenes – there are no questions asked and little judgement offered. I know plenty of older men who are getting much more sex than their teenage equivalents. For one thing they know where to look, how to ask for it and how to react when it's offered; they are probably more *au fait* with the etiquette of casual encounters and are often very versatile indeed.

In some countries, such as Thailand and the Eastern European states, age is still respected and youths will often feel that they have been honoured if attention is paid to them by an older man. In these countries, teenagers do not yet control the entire culture as they sometimes seem to here. Older gay men have a lot going for them if they keep an optimistic frame of mind.

Nevertheless, age can be cruel and even though the spirit is willing, the flesh can become weak. Arthritis can interfere with the ability to enjoy the more lively kinds of sex, and some drugs (such as those prescribed for hypertension, anaemia, diabetes and so on) can make it difficult to get or maintain an erection. But, with a little imagination, there is still plenty of scope for a very fruitful sex life.

One reassuring finding in the *Janus Report*, an American sex survey, was that more than half of the men questioned who were over 65 were having the same amount of sex as those aged 18-26. There was anecdotal confirmation of this in a letter which was published in *All Points North,* a gay magazine published in Leeds:

"I am over seventy and have been aware of my homosexuality since I was thirteen...The days of having a steady ongoing relationship with one person are over but the sight of a personable male today still makes me desire his attentions. If it is offered to me I am only too willing to fulfil any passive functions requested. Why I am sought out, I do not know, but all I have to offer is emotional and sexual relief. The same fellas always return for more and we enjoy our times together. Perhaps it's a case of understanding. Pecuniary gain never enters into our relationship but I have terrific sex. May it last and last."

I'll drink to that!

Groups to contact:

- Phoenix – for those who prefer mature men. Age range 21-85. Monthly personal ads. Regular newsletters. Social events. PO Box 103, Wallington, Surrey SM6 9SJ.
- September Group - guys 50-plus meet monthly. Call Michael 0171-221 4846 or Brian 01245 358881.

Agents Provocateurs

The Home Office issued new rules in the eighties telling the police that the use of *agents provocateurs* to entrap gay men having sex in public places was unacceptable. But arrests using this method are so easy that some police authorities still flout the rules and continue to send their best-looking, plain-clothes vice squad officers into cottages in order to provoke the unwary into compromising themselves. It all came to a head when a Tory politician was found in 'The Gay Theatre' in Soho one lunch time. A 'pretty policeman,' (as they came to be known) dressed provocatively in faded and tight jeans, allegedly invited the MP to touch his 'person'. The Tory responded by so doing and was then arrested and humiliated on the front pages of various scandal-sheets.

This is nothing new, of course. The first recorded *agent provocateur* was one Thomas Newton who, in the 1700s, was a regular visitor to Mother Clap's Molly House (q.v.). When it was raided and he was arrested, he was promised by the police that if he helped them catch other sodomites, he would be given his freedom. He resisted for a while, but eventually had to agree. In 1726, in an appearance at the Old Bailey, he described how he had gone along, with two policeman, to a notorious cruising ground – a path at Moorfields – and, with the policemen hidden close by, loitered with the intention of inciting other cruisers.

Giving evidence about that night, he said:

"In a little time the prisoner passes by, and looks hard at me, and at a small distance from me, stands up against the wall, as if he was going to make water. Then by degrees he sidles nearer to where I stood, till at last he comes close to me. Tis a very fine night, says he; Aye, says I, and so it is. Then he takes me by the hand and after squeezing and playing with it a little (to which I showed no dislike) he conveys it to his breeches, and puts—into it. I took fast hold and called out to (the police officers), who coming up to my assistance, we carried him to the watch-house."

The man entrapped in that instance was hanged. Perhaps the consequences of *agents provocateurs* aren't quite so lethal these days, although it is not unknown for men who are awaiting trial for 'sexual offences' to hang themselves.

One gay policeman who worked in London between the wars, wrote a book about his experiences. His name was Harry Daley and his memoir was *This Small Cloud*. He described the pleasure his colleagues got from setting up "nancy-boys".

"They hardly talked of anything else, working themselves into a non-stop giggling fit when they had an appreciative audience, sprinkling their anecdotes with 'dirty bastards' lest anyone should think they found pleasure in what they talked about so much. They were often struck off uniform duty and, slightly disguised, concealed themselves in the bushes and urinals on Putney towpath, bringing in triumphantly about once a fortnight a couple of lonely old gentlemen caught wanking one another off, and for the next month tittering and sniggering with their friends over the details."

In the constant battle between pleasure and hypocrisy, the sneaking, treacherous use of *agents provocateurs* must surely rank as one of the meanest tricks of all.

Group to contact:

- Gay Legal Advice, 0171-976 0840 (Mon-Fri 7-10pm) or write to them c/o 2 Greycoat Place, London SW1 1SB.
- GALOP, for men who have come into contact with the police for cottaging or queer bashing or any other reason: 0171-223 0854.

Unfortunately this topic cannot be avoided; it is inextricably linked with gay sex. However, it shouldn't be seen as a red flag which says "Don't go into the water". There is good news: AIDS doesn't necessarily mean that gay sex is going to kill you. With a constant and unwavering commitment to safer sex, you can avoid a brush with HIV. If you already have the virus, then you can protect yourself from further infection – and your partners from primary infection – by practising safer sex and *only* safer sex.

There is evidence emerging that gay men in the early '90s are beginning to tire of the safer sex message, or maybe the younger generation isn't getting it in the first place. Most sexually transmitted diseases can be avoided with the use of condoms. We must not waver in our efforts to survive to play another day.

More information:

- National Aids Helpline
  Tel: 0800 567 123

ALCOHOL

Most gay socialising and events revolve around alcohol. Pubs, clubs and discos all exist because the promoters make a profit from selling us drinks. Because of this, and of the emotional problems that afflict many gay men, the incidence of alcoholism in our community is higher than in many others.

I'm not going to moralise or lecture about alcohol – I like a drink or two myself – but let's face it: booze is a mind-altering drug! It can make us feel great, help us lose our inhibitions, it can add a great deal to a sexy encounter, but in excess it can also cause brewer's droop, stomach ulcers, liver failure and brain damage. Keep your alcohol intake under control. If your friends are telling you that you have a problem, listen to them. They can often see more clearly what is not apparent to you.

The recommended 'safe' intake of alcohol is currently 22 units per week for men (16 for women), but research is emerging that suggests that this will be increased. A unit consists of a half pint of beer, a small glass of wine or a single tot of spirits. The allowance should be spread over the whole week with perhaps one or two days off to let your body recover. You shouldn't take your quota all in one go – that will just destroy your stomach.

Having said that, a couple of drinks can create relaxation and enhance enjoyment of a sexual episode. More than a few and you're liable to find that you either aren't up to the job in hand or, more importantly, you're tempted to do something silly, like have unsafe sex.

It's pleasant to know that the latest research seems to indicate that a couple of drinks each day actually benefits the health.

Groups to contact:

- Inform-al – counselling for drink problems – Wednesdays 5.30-7.30pm, 23 New Road, Whitechapel, London E1. Tel: 0171-377 6915 for an appointment.
- Alcoholics Anonymous lesbian and gay group meets Thursdays 6.30-8pm, Ground Floor, Paterson Wing, St. Mary's Hospital, London W2. Tel: 0171-352 3001.
- Al-anon for the partners of problem drinkers. Tel: 0171-608 1471.

ALFRESCO SEX

Alfresco means out in the open, and often that's where gay men like to find sexual contacts. Hampstead Heath in London is probably the most famous venue for this kind of sex, but most towns and cities have their equivalent open air cruising ground. Some coastal areas in Britain and abroad have 'gay beaches'.

Beaches are popular trolling grounds because, of course, you are allowed to frolic there wearing next to nothing (and in some places nothing). They may be blessed with tall sand dunes which can protect you from prying eyes. The only drawback to seaside sex is that you might get sand in your condom which can be most irritating. (or, as the old joke goes: what do you call a man with sand in his johnny? Answer: an organ grinder).

In summer it can be wonderful to find erotic ecstasy under the sun, moon or stars, the warm breezes caressing those exposed areas can add an extra *frisson* to an outdoor hump. Watch out for grass burns, thorny bushes, nettles and inconvenient stones which can stick into awkward places. Be wary, also, of tutting straights who are out walking their dogs – they sometimes send for the police if the grunting, groaning and cries of 'shag me! shag me!' become too loud. Discretion is the keyword unless you're in a truly isolated spot – and there are precious few of those around in Britain.

AMATEUR NIGHT

A rather cruel colloquial term from the USA referring to a sexual encounter with an unskilled lover. Mae West's most famous put down to a journalist was: "Come up and see me sometime. Make it Wednesday. That's amateur night."

AMSTERDAM

The last flight from Amsterdam to London on Sunday night is the gay special. Gay men from all over Britain are returning from a weekend in what many regard as paradise. Sex, for the Dutch, is just another appetite and nothing to make a big deal about. Gay sex is, for the most part, regarded in much the same way as the straight variety. Gay cafes, clubs, bookshops, saunas and other facilities are situated on the main streets and no-one thinks much about them, except the people who want to use them.

What a relief from the tight-arsed sex culture we have in Britain. Can you imagine a porn shop in this country displaying its wares openly in the window facing on to a main street? In Amsterdam you can stop for a bit of voyeurism while out shopping, and hard core pictures appear in the windows of these shops. No problem for Dutch kiddies to get a decent sex education.

In Amsterdam, too, there is the world's first Sex Museum, a collection of erotica, pornography and equipment from down the ages. It's a fascinating place and after half an hour or so you come to realise that there's nothing in the world of sex that hasn't been tried before. The only difference between now and then is that these days we might be prepared to talk about it more.

Such easy-going attitudes to sex in the Netherlands makes it tempting to make comparisons between there and Britain. What are the effects on children of this openness – almost indifference – to sex and soft drugs? Well, Holland does seem to be a cultured country, with a good education system, and a communal interest the arts. There are social problems, of course, but not many of them are connected with sex. Rape is far less common than in Britain and child sex abuse is also rarer. People tend not to become obsessed and secretive about sex as they do in Britain and so it is less likely that such secrecy will lead to sexual abuse or violence.

The British have something to learn from the Dutch experiment, but I somehow don't think they will.

Anal masturbation

Some people can induce an orgasm simply by stimulating their arse. Rimming or fingering are, of course, the most common means of achieving this, followed by vibrators and dildoes. Not all of us are so sensitive "down there" that we can be brought off simply by being rimmed or digitally fucked, but it's horses for courses.

Anal violin

This refers to an anal masturbation device popular in oriental countries. It consists of a hard-boiled egg or wooden or ivory ball to which catgut is tied. The egg or ball is pushed into the anus, the string is pulled taut and a sex partner uses a violin bow to make the whole thing vibrate. I'm told this contraption was especially popular among the eunuchs of the Ottoman Empire.

It's one way to play beautiful music, I suppose.

Androgyny

In human terms it means an individual who displays characteristics of both sexes. You often hear the term 'androgynous' in the gay world, especially when someone likes to dress in drag or is effeminate. More subtly, the term is applied to pretty young men who have smooth skins, big eyes, delicate features and other characteristics which are regarded as attractive when they occur in women. Just as some straight men are turned on by the idea of 'deflowering' virgins, so some gay men find pretty youths particularly alluring.

In zoology, androgynous means hermaphrodite – that is, an animal or human being that has both male and female reproductive characteristics. The term hermaphrodite is derived from Greek mythology, Hermaphrodite being the son of the gods Hermes and Aphrodite. When Hermaphrodite spurned the love of a nymph, she embraced him with such vigour that their bodies became fused into one – literally two people in one body.

People who display characteristics of both sexes are regarded in many cultures as having mystical powers and are respected and even venerated.

Arousal

Sexual arousal in men is pretty obvious – it usually consists of the penis getting bigger and harder. When you're sexually aroused there is a release of the male hormone into your bloodstream and the manager of that little sperm bank between your legs starts preparing for a withdrawal of funds. You may become breathless and your temperature will go up. Some men find that the release of adrenaline which accompanies arousal causes them to tremble. The pupils of the eyes dilate.

Arousal is an individual thing, much quicker for some men than others. Some chaps – particularly adolescents – find that they have a renegade penis that seems to have a mind of its own. Up and down it goes like a yo-yo, lifting off at the most inconvenient moments.

Sometimes just riding on a bus can cause the sap to rise, and most of us have had embarrassing experiences at school when peter has decided to take a stretch at some awkward moment, such as during morning prayers. Older men might need a bit of coaxing and foreplay before the steamer occurs.

Involuntary stiffies can also manifest themselves during sleep, and you'll find more about this phenomenon under Nocturnal Erections.

ARSE

There are few things more pleasing than a firmly rounded and perky male bottom. Everyone has one, of course, but it's very much a matter of some men being more equal than others. The arse is, for gay men, a primary sexual characteristic and as such has to be made the most of. I'd put a pound to a penny that it was a gay man that designed the bomber jacket (or bum-freezer as it was affectionately known in former times); this puts the goods on display to great effect. Indeed, in physique photographs the male models are often wearing leather bomber jackets and nothing else, thus drawing attention to the largest muscle in the body, namely the *gluteus maximus*.

The wonderful thing for the connoisseur of the dinky derriere is that it can be freely observed almost anywhere, but there are definitely superior viewing points – looking up the stairwell of a double-decker bus, for instance. When a youthful pair of jeans makes for the upper deck, much pleasure can be obtained from watching the cheeks rubbing together from this interesting angle. Telephone boxes are also a good vantage point. When a hunk is talking intently on the phone he tends to place most weight on one leg. This causes the cheeks to sit at an angle – one up and one down – and has been known to distract the attention of passers-by to the extent that they have walked into lamp posts (and I still have the broken nose to prove it). Cinema queues tend to attract attractive bums. I invariably stand behind a butch, blond-haired beauty with particularly bouncy hind-quarters. It takes great restraint when in the proximity of such temptation not to just reach out and take a couple of handfuls.

Whether you like them small, flat and neat or big and round and muscular, you'll find them walking the streets as brazen as you like. Some gay men fancy the sort of bum that has slightly parted cheeks, given emphasis by the ribbing on jeans. Others prefer the globular type, which are wonderful when in their prime, but can rapidly sag if neglected.

Particularly favourite varieties of arse can be found on sportsmen. People like Daley Thompson have what aficionados call Athlete's Arse (which has no connection whatsoever to the much less desirable athlete's foot). Runners can develop sinewy, stringy legs and bottoms, and now that they have taken to wearing Lycra shorts, little imagination is required to imagine how the arse would perform if it were unfettered and free to bounce. Video recordings of athletics meetings can be enhanced by the use of the slow motion button, which demonstrates just how much jewellery is jangling inside those shorts.

Then there's Ballet Dancer's bottom. Male dancers often have bums of gigantic proportions, but shapely. This comes about because they spend so much time working on the barre. They fill their tights beautifully, both back and front (though sometimes the front takes a bit of believing).

The Polytechnic Posterior also has a following. This is the undeveloped kind, almost flat. Usually perched atop very thin legs, it is the particular domain of students and other young men who don't take proper care of themselves. Although their legs often resemble denim encased spaghetti, there are definite fans of the undernourished undergraduate.

The sure sign of a straight man is the visibility of bum cleavage. This is most often seen on navvies who are digging up the road. Bum cleavage invariably goes with a beer belly, saggy tits and dishevelled hair. Persons with visible bum cleavage are generally coarse and vulgar, and spend most of their time harassing passing women and making homophobic remarks to men they don't like the look of. Yuk!

As well as being a thing of beauty and, if you're lucky, a joy for ever, the arse can also be the source of much erotic stimulation. The many and varied attentions which can be paid to this particular erogenous zone are explained under other headings (See Fingering, Fucking, Rimming, Sex Toys etc.), but it as well to understand why we get so much pleasure from what many of our straight and narrow friends consider to be simply a channel of evacuation.

As you already know from your explorations and experience, the anus is a very sensitive spot. It has many nerve endings which give erotic pleasure when stimulated; these sensations seem to culminate right on the end of the cock. It is the prostate gland (q.v.) which helps to make anal sex such a pleasurable experience.

Anyone who has inserted a vibrator while masturbating will know that the sensations are intensified – sometimes almost unbearably so – when the orgasm arrives. This is all thanks to your little old prostate gland, which is situated up the arse, near the bladder. Sexologists have identified the 'G-spot' in women which, if stimulated, increases sexual pleasure. It is thought that this is a residual prostate gland.

In older men the gland often gets enlarged, blocking the urinary passage, and necessitating surgical intervention. So make the most of it while it's in good working order. And remember, some research has shown that prostate conditions can be worsened if you deny yourself regular sexual release in the form of an ejaculation.

Auto-erotic asphyxia

It has long been rumoured that a sexual thrill can be had from asphyxiation – or depriving yourself of air for a short period. It is called auto-erotic asphyxia or anoxia (in America, the youths who try it also term it 'scarfing') and by tightening a noose around the neck, the oxygen supply to the brain can be restricted, thereby causing sexual excitement. The effect has been noticed in people who have been executed by hanging. An old English poem reads:

The townsfolk saw with great dismay
His organ rise in boldest way,
A sign to all who stood around,
That pleasure e'en in death is found.

Many people have experimented with self-strangulation as a means of erotic stimulation, and it has a long history. It was recorded among the Mayas of ancient Mexico and known among the pre-Christian Celts in Britain. Needless to say, it can be extremely dangerous. There are several deaths each year as a result of people trying these things. A case was reported in *The Daily Telegraph* concerning a young Catholic priest who had been experimenting with asphyxia. He had tied himself to his bed with a noose round his neck and had, somehow, tried to strangle himself for kicks. It had all gone wrong and he ended up dying in these horrible circumstances.

The death of Tory MP, Stephen Milligan also caused a sensation in 1994 when it was discovered that his anoxia session had gone horribly wrong.

What is not realised by people who are trying these things as a masturbation aid is that when pressure is put on the vagus nerve in the neck, instantaneous death can occur. The sudden increase in the pressure sends a message to the heart to shut down and a sudden cardiac death can result.

There are no reliable statistics about how many people die every year from auto-erotic asphyxia, but in America one study estimated that there are between 500 and 1,000. An analysis of 135 such cases showed that the average age of the victim was 26. Most of them were heterosexual and often when their bodies are found there are other elements of sexual experimentation in evidence – bondage, cross-dressing, drug-taking and mirrors for self-observation. There is usually evidence at the scene that it is a frequently practised activity.

The worst thing about these deaths is that the thrill that was being sought may not actually exist. Although sexual arousal has been noted in men being executed by hanging, The Kinsey Institutes New Report on Sex, published in 1990, says that *"no research has ever verified"* the belief that auto-erotic asphyxia enhances orgasm.

If you're moving in this area be extremely careful. Every kind of self-rescue device, from slip knots to padding around the neck, has failed somebody in the past.

And now those people are just statistics in the coroner's court.

AUTO FELLATIO

Now this is a real speciality – sucking yourself off. You need a pretty supple back to be able to bend over sufficiently to get your cock in your own mouth and still have breath left to suck it.

But some people can do it. Mostly they lay on their back, put their legs over their heads and in that way manage to double themselves over sufficiently to make cock and mouth meet.

I suppose it makes a pleasant change from wanking, and in these days of environmental concern, recycling the cum is bound to be eco-friendly. If you are going to try it, be careful – it can prove an expensive thrill. Human backs are notoriously fragile and my own efforts to try this (purely in the interests of research, of course) cost me a small fortune in fees at the osteopath.

BACK ROOMS

Some bars and clubs in Europe and America (but not in Britain) have back rooms which are given over to sex. Usually they are dark, sometimes with black-painted walls. Participants drift in and out, have anonymous, orgiastic sex, and then return to the main body of the establishment for another drink. In back rooms, anything goes sexually – so long as you can manage to do it in the dark, and you aren't bothered about seeing who you're doing it with.

Backrooms, bath houses and saunas, which were used for quick and casual sexual gratification, became the target of moralists who blamed them for the spread of Aids when the disease first hit the headlines. For a while such establishments fell out of fashion, but now they're back, and many have introduced strong safer sex policies. While the proprietors often provide the condoms, they cannot enforce their use. That's up to the individuals concerned.

Orgy rooms are most easily found and tolerated in bars in Holland and Germany.

BALDNESS

Baldness is one inheritance that many men would prefer not to get from their fathers, and when it begins to develop it can prove an extremely hard blow to an individual's confidence. Male Pattern Baldness is genetic, so if your father was bald (or had a particular pattern of partial baldness) by the time he was twenty, thirty or forty, then you may well follow suit – but then again, the gene that causes this can skip generations, and affect some brothers and not others.

Male Pattern Baldness or androgenic alopecia affects at least 50% of the adult male population and about 10% of women. It is caused by the male hormone androgen. Androgenic hormones are responsible for the development of muscle and voice change and the ability to grow beards. They are mainly manufactured by the testes under the direction of the pituitary gland.

If you draw the genetic short straw, there is little you can do about it, and patent medicines which promise the contrary are generally phoney.

However, there is one concoction that has had some success and that is Minoxidil, which is sold under the name Regaine. It is the only product licensed as a hair restorer. A six month supply costs about £150 and there are no guarantees that it will be money well spent The longer the baldness has been present the less likely it is to work. Minoxidil is a vasodilator, which means it encourages blood supply to the area on which it is applied. Naturally, someone came up with the suggestion that it might help those with erection problems if applied to the penis. Experiments are under way, but no recommendations have emerged so far.

Those thinning on top can also have transplants, implants, toupees and wigs, all of which tend to cause more embarrassment than the baldness they are intended to hide. There have also been numerous cases of hair implants going painfully wrong, causing alarming reactions in the scalp and eventually leading to permanent scarring. There have also been success stories, of course, as anyone who followed the saga of Elton John's attempts to beat baldness will realise.

Save yourself a lot of cash, as well as humiliation and worry, by 'coming out' as bald, and making the most of it.

A lot of gay men think that receding hair makes them look older. Maybe it does, but that isn't necessarily a disadvantage. Many gay men have stopped combing their hair in eccentric ways in order to hide their bald patches, and have simply gone in for those close-cut styles which accentuate the shape of the head and reduce the importance of the hair. It's an effective way of dealing with a perennial problem.

Skinheads, after all, actively get rid of their hair and have an appeal for those who are looking for a bit of rough. There is something exaggeratedly masculine about a shortage of hair, and that's hardly a disadvantage in the gay world.

Balinitis

Balinitis is an inflammation on the glans – or head – of the penis, and the surrounding foreskin. It can look much more serious than it is, with lots of red and yellow pus-filled spots. It is not necessarily sexually transmitted, but it can be. Treatment is usually by a course of antibiotics.

Balls

There are few sights more appealing or exciting than a handsome pair of bollocks. Like other items of sexual equipment, they occur in an endless variety of shape and size. Some are small and close to the body, others are heavy and hang low, swinging in a most appealing fashion during activities involving pelvic thrusts. The left is usually larger than the right, and tends to hang slightly lower. The opposite is true of left-handers. (This puts me in mind of a Chinese take-away I knew called Won Hung Lo. It may have been anatomically correct, but it didn't make the chicken and cashew nuts taste any better.)

There are good reasons why the testes (singular: testis) are situated between the legs (as opposed to, say, under the nipples). For one thing they are less likely to get bashed about if they are protected by the inner thighs.

It is the function of the testicles to manufacture sperm and also the hormone testosterone, which is responsible for the sexual characteristics of the male body. So, you see that those little egg-shaped objects – attractively packaged in their neat little scrotal sac – are very important. It also explains why castration is a subject too fearful for most men to contemplate. The scrotum acts as a sort of thermostat for the balls; it lowers the testicles when your body is too hot and pulling them close when it is cold. If the testicles become too warm, they cease to function properly.

Of course, testicles are very sensitive and don't always take kindly to rough handling. Many men become tense and nervous when their goolies are approached. Most of us have had some experience of having them banged – either in a sporting accident or some other mishap – and there are few pains as excruciating. Some men feel so nervous when their balls are fondled that they can only tolerate very gentle licking and sucking. Other men, however, appreciate a bit of reasonably heavy squeezing and pulling and find that having their balls played with is an unending source of pleasure.

Gay lovers will always endeavour to make use of all available items of equipment, but you should approach your partners nuts carefully. Ascertain exactly what level of play he likes in this particular ball game by starting gently and gradually increasing the pressure. At the first sign of a wince or a squeal of pain, begin to scale down the pressure.

Many gay men like to have their lover straddle their face with the balls hanging over their mouth. They can then pay long, loving attention with the tongue, jiggling and occasionally sucking them one at a time or together while their partner masturbates. Once again, the tolerance levels vary greatly, so always ensure that your partner is not squirming in agony or fear ('Suppose he has a spasm in his jaw and it clenches shut while he's sucking my nuts?' he might be thinking).

However passionate you become in your search for new and exotic experiences, never be tempted to abuse the balls. If they are twisted and pulled too roughly, there is a small chance of a torsion – when all the tubes become twisted and strangulated – cutting off the blood supply. This can lead to one or both having to be surgically removed. You could still function perfectly well with one ball, or even no balls, but it's not a pleasant topic to contemplate.

You should check regularly for testicular cancer (q.v.). If you feel any unusual lump or bump in your balls, report it immediately to your doctor. If one balls suddenly balloons alarmingly, it could be a hydrocele – a collection of fluid in the tissue around the balls. This too should be treated by your doctor.

Tall men are particularly prone to varicoceles – literally varicose veins of the balls. It affects one in four men over six feet tall. They rarely cause trouble, but you should have them checked out by your doctor all the same.

Shakespeare described the testicles as balls, but spelt it 'bawls'. Other terms include rocks, diamonds, jingle-berries, and *cojones* (Spanish).

Groups to contact:

- Progress – a support group for men with penis and testes related problems – PUK, PO Box 31, Aldridge, Walsall, Staffs WS9 8RH (enclose s.a.e.).

- Fascinating fact: The world's first testicle transplant happened in 1977 in St Louis Missouri, when surgeons transplanted a testicle between identical twins, one of whom had two balls and the other none.

BATHROOM

Most people have had sex in the bathroom. It has erotic connotations because (a) it's the place most of us began experimenting with masturbation in our youth and (b) there are lots of interesting things you can do with running water. Having a session under a warm shower can be most revealing. Fucking someone while the water trickles down your back is a wonderful experience. The sensory input rejigs all the sensations and shifts them to different, and unusual, parts of the body.

Then there is the possibility of a submerged shag which, again, can be quite a treat, if somewhat limiting. Unless you have your own private swimming pool, it is likely that your underwater experimentation will be in the bath. In such cramped circumstances there is only so much that can be comfortably achieved. Be careful, if you put your partner's legs in the air, that his head doesn't disappear under the water.

And don't neglect the sink. Make sure it is secure enough to take your weight, and then see what you can manage with one of you sitting in the bowl. And, of course, the floor of the bathroom can be particularly interesting, especially if you possess the luxury of shag-pile toilet surrounds. Jacuzzis, too, with their swirling waters, also have their fans.

B & D

The code term for bondage and discipline. See S & M.

- Sir! Magazine for devotees of CP, B&D etc. Send name and address with two loose first class stamps to: PO Box 2153, London E7 0JZ.

Bears

The Americans seem to need a name for everything, and so it came to pass that hefty, mature men with a hairy faces and bodies were categorised as 'bears'. This 'look' has become very popular with some sections of the gay community and the rugged, unkempt outdoor type has become a recognised gay icon. So, the 'bear' can mean something that is untamed and wild but at the same time cuddly and cute (as in teddy bear).

- Group to contact: Bears Club UK – which welcomes "hairy guys and their admirers" – 56 Albert Street, Beswick, Manchester M11 3SU.

Beaumont, Chevalier Charles de

Born in 1728 and raised to wear girls clothes, this French nobleman and proficient swordsman was one of history's most famous transvestites. He never lost his preference for ladies garb and often wore it in his career as a spy. His transvestism was so convincing that many people believed that he was, in fact, a woman who occasionally dressed in men's clothes.

Bestiality

Having sex with animals (or inter-species sexual activity to give it its posh name) is nothing new. In olden times, when agriculture was a big part of everyone's life, relieving yourself with your favourite goat, sheep, pig or cow was quite common. After all, being a shepherd or a cowhand was a pretty boring business, spending every day watching your charges eat grass would be enough to drive anyone to the wearing of wellingtons. All the same, those caught in the act usually came to a nasty end – either hanged, burned, garrotted or jailed.

Kinsey estimated that 17% of men who worked on farms had sex with animals at some point.

The legendary size of the horse's dong (as in 'to be hung like a...') has also led some people to show an interest in our equine friends. And our canine companions are also frequently the object of loving affection, giving a whole new meaning to the term 'man's best friend'.

More exotic use has been made of animals. Tales reach me of gay men in the US employing de-clawed mice stuffed into velvet bags in a fashion that would not please the RSPCA, while a recent court case indicated that dolphins are not averse to a bit of slap and tickle from their human admirers, male or female. I also recently came across another case, reported in a London newspaper, of a man travelling on the tube with a cat on his lap – his fly was undone and his knob was nowhere to be seen. The cat was purring contentedly and the man was fined £200. The archaic legal name for bestiality is buggery.

I think my favourite anecdote on this subject was written by John Kenneth Galbraith: "One day the object of my love came to visit my sisters. We walked through the orchard and climbed on to a rail fence which overlooked a small field. Our cows were pasturing on the second-growth clover. With them was a white bull. As we perched there the bull served his purpose by servicing the heifer. Noticing my companion was watching with evident interest, and with some sense of my own courage, I said: 'I think it might be fun to do that.' She replied: 'Well, it's your cow.'"

BIGOT

A bigot was originally a 16th century religious maniac who was unable to see beyond his particular narrow creed. Four hundred years later there seems to be more of them than ever. Once bigots used to specialise in persecuting racial minorities but now that's become socially unacceptable, they've declared war on homosexuals.

To survive, extreme religionists need an enemy. They need a group they can stigmatise as 'evil' in order to wage a holy war against them. They need a rallying point for their barmy army. The communists used to fit the bill perfectly, but now they're more or less gone, there's got to be another focus for their hatred. Well, boys, we're it. Bigots seem particularly concerned with our sexual activities, which they describe as "unnatural", "abnormal" and so on. They are particularly fascinated by arse-fucking (or sodomy as they like to thunder), and spend a great deal of time thinking about us doing it, and telling other people how disgusting it is.

Not all bigots are heterosexual.

Bigots hang out in a twilight world, where they gather together to encourage each other in their evil practices. One of the twentieth century's most famous clubs for bigots was the National Viewers and Listeners Association, founded by a very strange and obsessed woman called Mary Whitehouse. But the NVLA's extremism is being superseded by that of The Conservative Family Campaign, an organisation one of whose membership requirements seems to be the possession of an extremely dirty mind. Wherever people might be having fun, bigots will appear as if out of the woodwork intent on putting a stop to it. They are always on the front-line of censorship campaigns and drives to outlaw sexual practices which they consider unholy.

Such groups are not new, of course. In 1691 an organisation called The Society for the Reformation of Manners was founded by a bunch of maniacal Christians to persecute 'prostitutes, pornographers, sodomites, Sabbath-breakers, swearers and the lewd.'

The Conservative Family Campaign, Family and Youth Concern and all the other modern-day anti-sex crusades can rightly claim the Society for the Reformation of Manners as their true ancestor. For many years the Reformation of Manners Society denounced the libidinous, and several 'sodomites' were hanged as a result of its campaigns. However, when it attempted to close down straight brothels, there were riots in the streets.

The Society for the Reformation of Manners had some of its bigger successes in tracking down Molly Houses (q.v.) and having them raided by the authorities.

It would benefit modern-day clean-up campaigners to remember what became of some of their 18-century counterparts. Charles Hitchen, for instance, who was the Under-Marshall to the City of London and an activist for the Reformation Society. He had "taken a world of pains and spent a great deal of money in discouraging profaneness, curbing the vices, and reforming the manners of the present age." In 1727 he was convicted of attempted sodomy and fined £20, condemned to the pillory and imprisoned for six months. A classic case of a gay man denying his own desires and punishing others for his own 'sins'. Seems those who came after – including the disgraced American televangelist Jim Bakker – did not learn from the mistakes of their predecessors in the self-righteousness stakes and had to find out the hard way. Mr Bakker built a huge empire on his anti-sex (particularly anti-gay sex) campaigns. He is now in prison for fraud and during his trial he was exposed as a bit of a sex maniac. His appalling wife Tammy escaped the wrath of the law, but hopefully not of the neighbours.

Other wicked bigots include those who put Pyotr Ilyich Tchaikovsky – one of the most popular composers in the world – through a kangaroo court, because of his homosexuality. The great man was, it is said, having an affair with the nephew of Count Stenbok-Fermor, a friend of the Tsar. When the Count threatened to kick up a stink about the affair, Tchaikovsky was summoned to a 'court of honour' and there he was told to choose between suicide or dishonour. Tchaikovsky, a sensitive man by all accounts, chose suicide and took arsenic to satisfy the bigots. Consequently, intolerance, filthy mindedness and just plain homophobia robbed the world of one of its brightest lights.

Another famous victims of bigotry, Oscar Wilde, said: "I have never come across anyone in whom the moral sense was dominant who was not heartless, cruel, vindictive, log-stupid and entirely lacking in the smallest sense of humanity. Moral people, as they are termed, are simple beasts."

BISEXUALITIES

Bisexuality has been defined as 'the capacity to feel sexual attraction toward and to consummate sexual performance with members of the opposite and one's own sex.' The idea that bisexuals get the 'best of both worlds' doesn't really stand up to examination, as complications and divided loyalties can play havoc with emotional lives.

There is also the added burden of doubt from some members of the gay community who say that there is no such thing as a bisexual, just gay people who are scared to come out as completely homosexual.

The sex researcher Alfred Kinsey, however, put it this way: "Males do not represent two discrete populations, heterosexual and homosexual. The world is not divided into sheep and goats. Not all things are black and white. Only human beings invent categories and try to force facts into separate pigeon holes. The living world is a continuum in each an every one of its aspects. The sooner we learn this concerning human sexual behaviour, the sooner we shall reach a sound understanding of the reality of sex."

On the Kinsey scale of human sexuality (see under Heterosexual/ homosexual), most people fall under the wide heading of 'bisexual'. 3 on the scale is the 'ideal' place to be in many people's estimation. It is defined as those who 'accept and equally enjoy both types of contact, and have no strong preferences one way or the other.' Kinsey 2's and 4's have a stronger preference either towards homosexuality or heterosexuality. It follows that there are more ways than one to be bisexual – hence the heading bisexualities.

Group to contact:

- Bi Helpline 0181 569 7500 (Tues & Weds 7.30-10.30pm)

BLINDFOLD

An essential piece of equipment used in S&M scenes. The use of the blindfold can increase the sense of power of the master and helplessness of the slave.

BLOW JOB

Also called sucking off, mouth fucking and 'going down' on someone. It is one of the all-time favourite sexual activities between men (although it's a mystery to me why it's called a *blow* job when it mainly involves sucking). Project Sigma found that 97 per cent of its respondents had been either the receptive or insertive partner in cock-sucking. The term fellatio, although widely used to describe *all* cock-sucking, actually refers to the practise of the sucker doing the movements. When the sucker remains still, and the inserter does the thrusting, the correct term is *irrumation*.

The joy of cock-sucking is that it can be performed with very little preparation, in restricted circumstances, without the need to remove clothing. This makes it excellent for those meeting alfresco or in cottages. Getting down on your knees to worship at the shrine does not involve anything more elaborate than opening a fly.

However, if the circumstances are more conducive to relaxation and time-taking, the variations on fellatio are many. One partner can stand while the other kneels. One partner can straddle the shoulders of the other. The sucker can lie on his back to allow the suckee easy access. Mutual blow-jobs, which are also very popular, are known as sixty-nines. It gives the best of both worlds, and what more could you ask?

The good news is that most Aids educators think that, with a little care and attention, sucking is a relatively safe activity as far as the spread of HIV is concerned. It's best not to let people come in your mouth, but if that particularly turns you on, then ensure that you don't have any cuts, sores or ulcers on your tongue or gums or inside your cheeks.

If you are sucking off someone whose health status you don't know, then it is probably better for them to wear a condom. You can get fruit flavoured johnnies which are more pleasant to suck on than the traditional rubber flavoured ones. Nobody has yet produced a cock-flavoured condom – if they did it would be a best-seller.

If you are using condoms for sucking, be careful that you don't use the kind that are treated with spermicides, as these can irritate the throat. If you don't have any cuts, rashes or skin lesions, then it is perfectly OK for him to pull out at the last moment and shoot his load all over your face. There is something particularly appealing about this for many men who like to feel the warm jism sliding down their cheeks or off the end of their chin. Try not to get it in your eyes, though.

If you are sucking, make sure you don't scratch or nick your partner's cock with your teeth. If you're lucky to have a really long cock to work on, it is possible that it will push well into your throat. Deep throat sucking is quite an art and for the uninitiated it could trigger a gag-reaction. Controlling this reaction takes a little bit of practice, but it can be done, and it is certainly more reassuring for your partner if you don't spend the whole time retching while you have his cock in your mouth. Don't forget that most of the sensations will be generated at the head of the cock, so be sure to give it a good hard licking, and sucking as it slides into your throat.

For those who become expert at cock-sucking, the problem of an aching jaw and tongue muscles is less of an issue than for those who only occasionally indulge. A prolonged session of fellatio can cause the tongue and face muscles to become painfully stiff: you are anxious not to stop, but fatigue sets in after about ten minutes. There is only one way to strengthen the requisite muscles, and that is to keep on exercising them. And that means sucking more cock.

It beats weight-training any day.

Blue balls

Sometimes called 'lover's nuts', this is a pain in the testicles caused by repeated sexual arousal without ejaculation.

It doesn't happen often and is easily relieved with a wank. It tends to be a problem more for younger people whose sexual feelings are in overdrive and often in need of urgent attending to.

Body dysmorphobia

This is a relatively new psychological condition, also known as 'imagined ugliness syndrome'. In its extreme form it can lead to people having unnecessary plastic surgery, developing anorexia and even committing suicide. People suffering from body dysmorphobia cannot look in a mirror and see what is really there. They imagine that their nose is too big, that their mouth is crooked or there is 'something wrong' with their eyes. They can have an exaggerated and distorted idea of their height and weight and a totally erroneous idea of the shape of their body, feeling themselves to be in some way deformed or 'not in proportion'.

With the amount of emphasis which is placed on physical beauty in the gay community, we can expect to see more cases of this condition. It can induce misery and depression in the sufferers who become absolutely convinced that they are so ugly that no-one could possibly fancy them. They can become reclusive, anti-social and lonely.

If you have the idea that you are 'too ugly' to compete in the gay market place, then just remember that your mind may be playing tricks on you. There are very few people who are so ugly that they can't find a partner anywhere.

And if you are considering cosmetic surgery, think carefully about whether it is really necessary. Ask an objective opinion before going ahead; get independent counselling if necessary. Too much surgery on the face can leave you looking really bizarre, as anyone who saw Liberace in his later years will testify.

BODY LANGUAGE

Body language is what we tell people by gesture, posture, facial expression and other non-verbal signals. In sexual terms there is a rich body language that human beings use with each other. However, the studies that have been done are usually about the body language between men and women, and it is difficult to know how much of this would apply to two men who were sexually attracted.

In overtly gay circumstances there is more directness. Everyone knows that everyone else is a potential partner and there is little scope for misunderstanding if you want to make a proposition to someone. In less overtly gay places, such as at straight parties and at work, you may be fancying someone but be unsure whether or not they are gay or whether the attraction is reciprocated.

Here are a few signs that might help you decide whether you're on the right track. Standing in close proximity to someone, for instance (invading their personal space) is a signal that increased intimacy is desired. So, if you are at a party and someone is chatting to you and they stand nearer than, say, eighteen inches, then you can rest assured that they're telling you that they'd like to get even closer. Their proximity will usually be accompanied by a long look into your eyes (this can be seen as aggressive in some situations, but it is easy to tell the difference), and by occasional glances downwards in the general direction of your crotch. You can check whether someone would welcome an advance from you by standing within their personal space. If they move back to increase the space, forget it. If they stay put, then you can proceed with confidence.

Another body language signal that someone is fancying you is if they mirror your actions. If you both have a drink, for example, he will sip from his glass at the same time that you do. If you cross your legs, so will he, and so on. The technical term for this is *building a rapport*.

Signs that you are barking up the wrong tree (he may be straight or simply doesn't fancy you) is if he repeatedly glances over your shoulder while you're talking to him, if he fails to maintain eye contact for at least fifty per cent of the time, if he turns at an angle away from you, folds his arms, crosses his leg away from you or maintains a distance of more than eighteen inches. If he says "yes" but accompanies it with a tiny head shake or eye wobble, he may be being economical with the truth. Hiding his lips with his hand is another negative signal.

Other signs to look out for: If he touches his lips soon after meeting you, he is signalling sexual interest – coupled with fear of rejection. If he rubs the back of his neck or his stomach, he is massaging away intensity of emotion. If he suddenly withdraws and gazes into the distance, he is unconsciously retreating to test if you will follow. Continue to flirt, even though he seems to have retreated.

Men like to sit with their legs apart, directing attention to their crotch. If you see someone glancing at your crotch, don't take it as an immediate indication that they'd like to get their face in there. Men often make comparisons and like to see what the competition is offering. So, straight men like to look at baskets, too.

Bottom man

This usually refers to the man who is taking the passive or receptive role in any given sex act. Of course, a man who is being fucked need not necessarily be on the bottom – sitting on the cock is a very popular position.

Many men, though, thoroughly enjoy being the object of other men's desires, and enthusiastically allow themselves to be made to love to. Traditionally, of course, men are supposed to be the aggressors in sex, always taking the initiative and dictating the action. This can be frustrating if you desire to be wooed, dominated and fucked. Even straight men, when they are being honest, say they would occasionally like their women to make the first move and get on top.

Gay men are not fixed into these roles and we can experience love-making from both points of view. There are some men, of course, who will only "do" and others who will only "have it done" to them. In many cultures this is because masculinity is not compromised by taking the "active" role in anal sex, but taking the "passive" or feminine role is thought of as intolerable. Often in prisons, heterosexual men will merrily fuck their fellow inmates, but may become violent and aggressive if there is a suggestion that they should get on the bottom. But for *real* gay men, the opportunity to fuck and be fucked in the same session holds a great appeal.

Boundary

This is important in these days of safer sex. We all need to know how far we are prepared to go with each individual person we have sex with, and we really should make an effort to ensure they understand our boundaries. Sometimes sex can get rough, and even violent. Passion can carry us away. We must be prepared to let our partner know what we are prepared to tolerate and what is beyond our personal limits. Most experienced practitioners of SM agree beforehand a signal that will tell them when the limits are reached. It would be a good idea if other lovers had a similar signal which they could use when things are getting dangerous or unpleasant. If, for instance, you don't want to dampen down excitement and spontaneity by discussing in detail beforehand what you are or are not prepared to do, then you could simply agree a signal between you – a pull of the hair or a slap on the bum, for instance – which says: "that's as far as it goes". For instance, if your lover is all greased up and prodding at your arse with his dick, but you have decided that you aren't going to be penetrated, then the signal could be quite easily made without interrupting the action. You're simply saying: "try something else".

This bodily signal might be more preferable to a verbal restraint. There is no doubt that the instant someone says "no" in a sexual encounter, some of the passion dissipates.

Boy marriage

Among the Australian Nambutji, every young man between 12 and 18 becomes the boy-wife of the man who performed his circumcision during initiation. Sometimes the boy performs the active role in homosexual sex and sometimes passive. He is later required to marry the daughter of his "husband". A similar carry on was to be found at the turn of the century among the people living round the Egyptian oasis of Siwa. Of course, several other cultures have also embraced the concept of young men and boys being partnered with older more influential men for education and sexual purposes. Perhaps the most famous example of that was the Greek model.

The *News of the World* would have a field day with anyone who attempted to introduce these quaint customs into Britain.

Breaking and entering

Prisons have much colourful slang. The American penal system has, of course, produced a different argot than our own dear Queen's institutions. Breaking and entering is slang for anal rape – an occupation which has reached legendary status in the US.

See also under jail sex

Brothels and bordellos

Brothels for male prostitutes have existed as long as the heterosexual equivalents. They are most openly advertised and easily located in Amsterdam where they are called Houses with Boys. They can also be found in Thailand, (see under Tourism) where there is no stigma attached to prostitution

See also under Mollie Houses and Peg Houses

- Book to read: *Mother Clap's Molly House* (GMP Publishers)

Buggery

Anal intercourse or sodomy by any other name would be buggery. The word is derived from "Bulgaris" because Bulgarian heretics were reputed to practice sodomy at one time. As a legal term it can also mean having sex with animals. In the 16th and 17th centuries, buggery had a much wider meaning and could encompass all types of 'debauchery' – heterosexual, homosexual and cross-species. See also Sodomy and Fucking.

Butch

The swaggering machismo which is the hallmark of our most violent oppressors is also one of the things that many of us find most attractive about men. It is a constant paradox of gay life that, even though the bruiser with the cropped head and Doc Marten's would just as soon kill us as look at us, he's the one that many of us would like to take to bed.

But is he butch? Or is he just a bit of rough? Butch is almost as hard to define as camp and, indeed, there are crossover points in the two apparently contradictory terms. The dude cowboy with the immaculately pressed fringe-shirt and brand new Levis may well have all the hall-marks of being butch (broad shoulders, craggy face, big, hairy hands) but something about his pristine appearance tips him into the realms of camp.

We all have our own fantasies of what constitutes butch, and we see those fantasies being acted out in gay venues all over the world. The hard-hatted workman with his tool-belt slung provocatively round his waist, the leather-clad motorcyclist, the tattooed skinhead, the jaunty sailor – all are icons of gay fantasy. But there's no substitute for the real thing, and many gay men walk by a building site with a sigh and a brief thought about gang-bangs in the Portakabin.

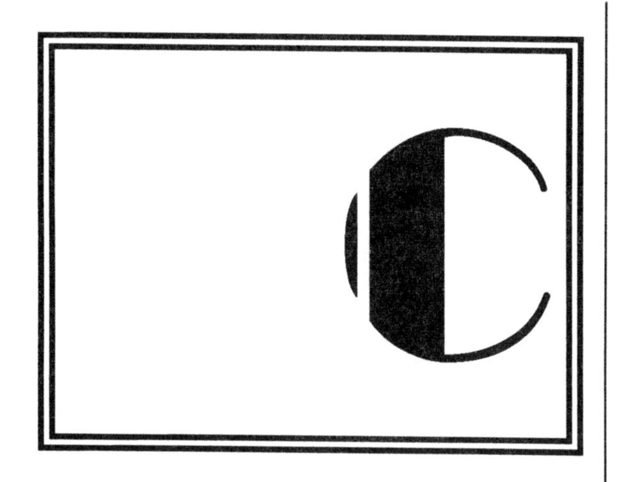

Camp

Describing camp is a difficult business, but one definition says it is 'taking frivolous things seriously and serious things frivolously'. We all have our own idea of what we regard as camp, whether it is an over-the-top movie performance from Bette Davis or Joan Crawford or a super-macho one from Jean-Claude van Damme or Dolph Lundgren. Anything that takes itself too seriously is open to demolition by camp innuendo. Oscar Wilde is often cited as an arch practitioner of camp, and his urbane, throw-away aphorisms certainly qualify. Quentin Crisp, a self-defined 'effeminate homosexual', raised the art of camp to new heights. Opera can be camp as can any other over-stated and histrionic art form.

The word is often used to describe stereotypical homosexual behaviour 'He's as camp as a row of tents' or 'The decor in here is as camp as Christmas'. 'Camp as arseholes' is a rather coarser variation on this theme.

People who set out to be camp often aren't. It takes an indirect approach to qualify. For instance, Larry Grayson the effeminate comedian who never directly addressed homosexuality in his act, is camp. But Julian Clary, who is a 'homosexual comedian', is not camp, despite his extravagant costumes and 'slap' (make up).

Book to read:

- *High Camp* by Paul Roen.

Celibacy

Most of us understand celibacy to mean 'not having sex', but technically a celibate is simply someone who has vowed never to marry. It is an archaic word which has changed meaning over the centuries. After all, the vast majority of unmarried people in this country could hardly be accused of refraining from sexual activity.

Of course, most celibates are so because they have a calling to the religious life. Monks are well known for swearing a lifetime of chastity, and equally well known for going up each other's cassocks at every opportunity.

Celebrated celibates have included Stephen Fry, Cliff Richard and Mother

Teresa of Calcutta, all of whom have sworn that they don't have sex. Most refrain from revealing what kind of sex they don't have.

The Catholic church insists that its priests remain celibate (because, you see, they are married to the church). This results in many of them either abusing children or leaving the church because after a couple of years of self-denial, the spunk is coming out of their earholes. The Vatican has said that gay sex is unnatural, but it can't possibly be as unnatural as choosing to live a life completely devoid of intimate contact with other human beings.

Perhaps the Pope's own celibacy goes some way to explaining why he's such an evil old git.

CHUBBY CHASER

Those who fancy the overweight and obese have been charmingly called 'chubby chasers' by our American brothers. Some gay men are turned on by seeing a meaty, well-nourished body and can't wait to get their hands on those love handles. Our advertising-dominated culture has imbued in us the idea that everyone has to have a particular shape in order to be attractive, which is why gymnasia up and down the country are packed out with gay men huffing and puffing on rowing, cycling and weight-lifting machines; and why psychiatric hospitals are overrun with young girls weighing three stones and insisting that they're as fat as pigs.

Our lifestyle goes some way to dictating our shape. Surely a bank manager was never meant to be built like Arnold Schwarzenegger, and it is reasonable that a librarian should have a couple of chins more than most and a bit of a podge. Who put the idea into our heads that we all have to have muscles like Adonis if we are to be sexy? Well, I'm not going along with it any more – away with the Bullworker! Shite to the steroids! I shall eat suet pudding and custard if I want to, and someone will surely find me attractive afterwards – won't they? Well, yes, a chubby chaser will. Thank God for them.

Groups to contact:

- Big Boys and Buddies, 18 Cookes Close, Leytonstone, London E11 3EF
- The Bulk Club UK, PO Box 1155, London SW2 1EE.

CIRCLE JERK

It simply means sitting round in a circle with a group of other men and either wanking your neighbour or yourself. It's an American invention in response to the Aids crisis, and has now been taken up in other European countries as a safer sex practice. Not in Britain, though, where our archaic laws forbid group sex.

Circle jerks give the participants the chance to have sex with other men without any chance of HIV being transmitted. In the USA, where circle jerk groups have become well-established, a complex etiquette is developing. Some circle jerk parties even have themes, for example people wearing particular items of fetish clothing, telling dirty stories, swapping sexual anecdotes or using sex toys on one another.

Groups decide whether they will allow touching and kissing or other forms of contact between participants. In case things get out of hand, others insist that looking and listening is all that is permitted.

In Amsterdam some of the bars are organising circle jerk nights, when everyone can be thoroughly outrageous without taking any risks. The success of the circles depends very much on how imaginative the participants are and how many of them are prepared to put on a good show.

Circumcision

Cut or uncut – an important aesthetic consideration for some men who have definite preferences in this area. Whether or not a man has retained his foreskin may be related to his religious upbringing. Jewish and Muslim men are circumcised as a matter of course at a very early age, and some other parents are absolutely convinced that circumcision is important for hygiene reasons. Modern medical knowledge doesn't share this view. So long as the cock is kept clean (by drawing the foreskin back and washing away any smegma which might have accumulated) it doesn't seem to matter whether it is cut or uncut. In Britain only something like 7% of males are circumcised (although in the USA the proportion is still very much higher), so the likelihood is that most men you meet will still come with foreskin attached. Only if there are problems drawing back the foreskin (phimosis, q.v.) do you need to seek medical advice, although you may wish to be circumcised for the sake of appearances.

The arguments rage endlessly about whether circumcised men get more pleasure from sex than their uncut brothers. There doesn't seem to be any convincing evidence either way.

If you need to be circumcised later in life, the operation can be done under local or general anaesthetic and takes about 20 minutes, often without the need for an overnight stay. It is available on the National Health Service.

Cleveland Street Scandal

The year: 1889, the place: London. A telegraph messenger boy named Charles Thomas Swinscow was questioned by police about how he came to have the sum of eighteen shillings on his person – a large amount in those days for such a modestly paid lad. He replied that he had been doing "private work" for a man called Hammond who lived at 19 Cleveland Street, north of Soho in London.

He had been invited to the house by another clerk named Henry Newlove, who was, like Swinscow, fifteen years old and worked in the same Post Office. It turned out that the two boys had been "behaving indecently" in a lavatory at their place of work, and Newlove had suggested to Swinscow that he could earn a bit of extra money by doing the same thing for gentlemen.

The two went to the house in Cleveland Street and got into bed with a gentleman who, according to Swinscow's police statement, "put his person between my legs and an emission took place". The gentleman paid a half sovereign for the privilege, and Swinscow gave it to Hammond, the owner of the house. Hammond gave him back four shillings, and recognising that he could make good money from having a good time, the boy became a regular.

It soon became apparent that there were lots of youths from the Post Office earning a second income at Cleveland Street. A seventeen year old, George Wright, was also invited by Newlove to Cleveland Street where the two of them got into bed with "a foreign looking man" who "had a go between my legs and that is all". Others simply "played with" gentlemen, and allowed gentlemen to "play with" them for their four shillings.

When the police raided the place, they discovered that it was boarded up and the owners had fled to France.

On further questioning, the boys admitted that some of their customers had been rich and important persons. Names included Lord Arthur Somerset, Colonel Jervois and the Earl of Euston. Further investigations revealed that the Duke of Clarence (known as "Eddy") who was son of the Prince of Wales, had also been named as a customer.

There then followed a complicated web of cover-up, deceit and establishment manipulation. The newspapers, however, were determined to get at the truth and The North London Press named names on 16th November, 1889. One of the names was the Earl of Euston, who immediately sued the editor of the paper for libel.

The defence produced several witnesses who swore that they had seen Lord Euston going in or out of 19 Cleveland Street, and the good Lord said that he had indeed been there, under the impression that there were to be performances of *poses plastiques* – naked girls posing in scenes from Greek mythology. When he discovered that no women were available, he claimed that he threatened the owner of the house with violence and then left.

The final witness in the trial was a rent boy by the name of John Saul, who claimed he had picked up Lord Euston and taken him to Cleveland Street. He said that Lord Euston was "not an actual sodomite. He likes to play with you, then spend on your belly."

The editor of the paper was found guilty of libel without justification and sentenced to a year in prison.

Lord Euston went to live in the south of France and stayed there under an assumed name until his death in 1926. Unlike those he had "played with" he did not face prison. Some of the lads got hard labour.

How things change – and yet how they stay the same. Goodness knows how many of our modern-day "Lordships" have been caught cottaging or fondling the stable boys and have got away with it because of their title or position. Believe me, I've nothing against the fondling of stable boys, but I've got an awful lot against a law which is applied differently for those with unearned privilege.

Book to read:

- *Ruling Passion* by Tom Driberg

Closet

Closet was originally a French word for 'little enclosure', hence its association with secrecy and concealment. The closet is a terrible, dark, frightening place which most homosexuals have inhabited at some time in their life; it is the place from which it is essential to escape at the very first opportunity. You can have sex in the closet, but it's never very joyful. The problem with being in the closet is that you are constantly apprehensive that someone is going to "find out" that you're in there and drag you out. Consequently, all contact with other homosexuals becomes dangerous. Many gay men who have not escaped the confines of the closet will deny, and even denigrate, their gay friends if the occasion demands it.

Any foray they make into the gay community will be fraught with worry. They will feel guilty about having sex with other men because generally they are betraying someone else's trust to do it. If mum and dad knew what they were up to! Or what if wife and kiddies ever found out? Or the boss at work? Or the police? Or the newspapers?

Getting out of the closet is not easy, but it can be done. And once the door is open, life becomes richer and much more tolerable. Opportunities for development open up. You can be yourself.

So, if you've nailed yourself into a closet, take a deep breath and kick the door down. Like any exotic plant, you'll need light to flourish.

Book to read:

- *How to be a Happy Homosexual* (GMP Publishers) is full of practical suggestions for successful Coming Out.

Cock ring

Cock rings come in various styles: metal, leather and improvised. The ring is pushed over the cock, and sometimes over the balls as well, so that when an erection is obtained, the ring restricts the flow of blood back down the penis, keeping it hard and erect. There is little danger from using cock rings if they aren't worn for too long and aren't too tight. A cock ring can be improvised from a piece of string or material such as a handkerchief. But be careful not to use anything too sharp, such as nylon thread, which might cut into the skin and cause injuries.

Colt

The Colt Studios of California became one of the pioneers of gay porn in the seventies. They peddled – and still do – the image of ultra-masculine men having sex with each other. Their models were mainly the pumped up, hyper-muscled hunks that have become so ubiquitous in present-day gay imagery. Colt were also one of the first studios to extensively feature leather as a sexual adjunct.

Colt models became a by-word for strength, smoothness, aggressive sexuality and physical perfection. No pimply youths with erection problems graced the Colt Calendar. Only the most well-developed creatures at the peak of their physical fitness were permitted to be identified with the Colt trade mark. A very particular style of photography was employed to promote the Colt philosophy and such acclaimed photographers as Jim French spent part of their career enhancing the image of gay men as demi-gods. Indeed, the art of photographing the male nude was raised to great heights through the aegis of Rip Colt (who was the supposed president of Colt Studios).

Then came the films. 8mm masterworks of homo-eroticism which were smuggled into this country and enjoyed by an increasingly appreciative audience. Not only were the Colt hunks beautifully constructed, they were exceedingly sexy when put into each other's company. The Colt style of film-making also differed from the run-of-the-mill porn, as there was less emphasis on penetration and anatomical close-ups, and more on the whole body experience. In many instances the actual penetration was hidden from view, but this did not seem to detract from the arousal factors of the films.

Many of the men who featured in the Colt studios output became 'stars' in their own right. Al Parker, Dakota, Mike Davies, Bruno, Toby – each had their own following. They tended to be the more mature (that is, up to about 35 years old) men, who knew what they were doing and were obviously well-experienced in the trade.

We hear less of the Colt studios these days, apart from their calendars, which are still masterpieces of erotic art. The production values they employed ensured that their magazines, films and posters were always of the highest quality.

Some Colt magazines and calendars from:

- The Zipper Store, 283 Camden High Street, London NW1 7BX

Compulsive sex

Loaded and judgmental terms like "promiscuity" have become meaningless in the present restrictive sexual climate, and some 'moralists' are quick to brand anyone who has more than one partner as 'promiscuous'. Who said that human beings are supposed to be monogamous, anyway? Why, some boring old fart in the Bible, that's who! But of all the millions of animal species on the planet, only a handful can be said to be monogamous, so the odds are stacked against the Bible-thumpers being right about this (or just about anything else, come to that). Simple observation of human behaviour seems to confirm that there are extremely few of us who get through life with only one partner.

Having said that, there are some gay men who have become addicted to sex in an unhealthy way. They compulsively seek out new partners, sometimes several each day. This is not particularly because they want sex all the time, but because their continuous sexual activity satisfies some psychological need. This is not the same as treating an ordinarily healthy sexual curiosity as some kind of illness.

Psychologists recognise that sex can become addictive, just like drugs. Persio Burkinsky, of the Centre of Integral Psychoanalysis in London, says: "Having sex can be a way to escape from something, to avoid facing facts." For many gay men, it isn't difficult to see what facts they're trying to avoid, what aspect of their lives they're running away from.

Such ceaseless and uncommitted bed-hopping is dangerous from several points of view – the most important being a greater likelihood of infection with HIV.

A man suffering from sexual addiction will have great difficulty in making or sustaining meaningful relationships because he will always have this overwhelming desire to seek ever more sexual partners. The sexually compulsive should think about seeking some kind of psychiatric intervention to help them get to the root of their problem. A healthy interest in sex is one of the joys of life, but when it becomes an uncontrollable obsession, it isn't so great.

Group to contact:

- Sexual Compulsives Anonymous. Tel 0181-914 7599 (based at St. Pancras Hospital, London).

CONDOM

Rubber, johnny, French letter, sheath, prophylactic, protective, jolly bag – all names for a simple, but marvellous idea. Shakespeare referred to them as 'Venus glove', while Casanova called them *redingote d'Angleterre* (English overcoats).

The earliest recorded version of the condom is in a cave painting at Les Combarelles, central France, dated 15,000 BC. After that, the idea seems to have disappeared until the sixteenth century when a version made from a pig's bladder softened in water was said to have been produced by Dr Quondam, a physician in the French royal court.

Also credited with the johnny's invention is an Italian anatomist Gabriel Fallopius, who gave his name to the fallopian tube. His condom consisted of a linen sheath soaked in oils. No-one is absolutely sure where the term 'condom' really originated.

In the sixties, when the Pill was the main form of contraception, and when gay men felt no need of precautions, the johnny fell from favour. Nowadays, because of Aids, and the reluctance of some women to take the Pill, it has enjoyed a revival. The manufacturers have risen to the challenge and have come up with several specialist condoms: extra strong ones, for instance, which will stand up to the rigours of anal sex, and fruit flavoured ones which give a whole new meaning to the phrase strawberries and cream – at least as far as cock suckers are concerned. Condoms are generally 52mm at the open end, but manufacturers are beginning to realise that cock sizes vary and they have now introduced a 49mm 'snug fit' version. There is also a 'magnum' version at 54mm.

Condoms can go a long way to saving you from HIV infection and, if you're already infected, to save other people. Condoms don't just protect against HIV, of course, but from many other sexually transmitted diseases, too.

Essential advice: make sure the use-by date has not been passed, and also that the condom carries the British Standard Kite Mark, which indicates it is of the highest quality.

To make sure the condom fits securely, always wait until your cock is hard before putting it on. Then, holding the tip of the condom between your finger and thumb, squeeze the air out so there's room for the cum and unroll it all the way down to the base of your cock with the other hand.

After coming, withdraw carefully while you're still hard, holding on to the base of the condom so that it doesn't leak or slip off.

Some of the more exotic sheaths – the ones with bobbles, toggles and ribbing for tickling purposes – are often of poor quality and may tear and or leak very easily. Some manufacturers are making 'extra strong' varieties which will withstand the rigours of anal sex. The German HT brand and Durex Extra Strong are two such. And there is also Gay Willie, the UK's first condom to be aimed specifically at the gay market.

Project Sigma, an ongoing study of the sexual habits of gay men, tried to find out why so many of us are resistant to the use of condoms. The main reasons were that condoms are a nuisance and inconvenient to use, interfere with sensation; interrupt sex and reduce spontaneity. There were objections to the feel, smell and taste of them, they were liable to break; were fiddly, uncomfortable and not sexy, felt artificial and – finally – the sensation of the cum was missing. Some people also objected to condoms on the grounds that they are associated with heterosexual sex! Others said it was like wearing a raincoat to sunbathe.

If you share the opinion that condoms are a turn-off, then get wise and start changing that perception. If you haven't tried them yet, buy a packet and play around with them. Have a wank with one on and see how it feels. Put one on your partner and see how it's done. Eroticise them and make them into an essential part of your love making. They aren't hard to come by these days, you can get them in garages, record shops, slot machines, mail order, hairdressers, as well as in chemists. . In some gay bars you can pick them up free of charge from the counter.

Use only water-based lubricants with condoms (KY is perfect). Oil-based lubricants (Vaseline, butter, vegetable oil, baby oil etc.) tend to rot the rubber and cause the sheath to disintegrate very quickly. Important as they are, condoms – unlike the Pope – are by no means infallible. They can come off, leak and tear. A much better approach is to try finding other kinds of sexual activity that don't involve penetration, and then you can be as free as a bird and as naked as the day you were born.

The National Aids Manual has printed guidelines for gay men using the female condom (brand name "Femidom") as a protective against HIV. The Femidom is made from polyurethane and can, therefore, be used with non-water based lubricants. It is a large sized sheath, which can be inserted into the anus (with the open end protruding) and thereafter, the man can be fucked with little formality and no fiddling about with condoms. An American study had shown that some male couples had used this method quite frequently and had experienced no problems with leaks or tearing.

The world of condoms is developing all the time, and there are now several specialist shops which can provide all the latest versions.

Where to get latest condoms:

- Condomania, The Yard, 57 Rupert Street, London W1. Mail order service available. Tel: 0171-287 2248.

CONTACT ADS

Contact ads in the gay press are a useful way of finding the kind of sex you want. You get a direct line to those who share your interests, which saves an awful lot of trolling round the bars and being disappointed that your latest catch doesn't like what you like.

In Britain there are limits to what you can say in your ad, but with a little imagination it is possible to get the message across to your waiting audience. *Boyz Magazine*, a weekly freesheet which can be picked up in some gay venues, and is also available on subscription, has a system of classification which gives you the opportunity to name your pleasure. Each personal ad can go under a heading such as 'Boots and Braces', 'City Gents', 'Leather', 'Firm Hand', 'Reel Men' (video), 'Splash Out' and so on.

Be careful about giving your name and address before you've checked people out. Whether you are advertising or responding to an ad, only give your telephone number and first name initially. Then arrange to meet on neutral territory.

Blind dates are high stress events (what if he doesn't like me? What if I can't stand him?), so you need to be a little assertive if you think things aren't quite what you were led to believe in his letter or phone call. For instance, he might have said he was a twenty-two year old, six foot, well-hung hunk, when in fact he is a Woody Allen look-a-like.

Computer Bulletin boards are also increasing in popularity as non-personal cruising grounds, as are voice-mail telephone dating agencies. There are also the traditional 'introduction agencies' operating on the gay scene, and you'll find some of them listed in the gay press.

Where to advertise:

- Gay Times, Ground Floor, Worldwide House, London NW1 OBA
- Boyz Magazine, 13 Hercules Street, London N7 6AT.

Cottaging

Cottaging is an age-old tradition which is still popular in many parts of the world. But what is the persistent appeal of trolling through the public lavatories for which Britain is so famous? Why do men still do it in these days of liberation, when there are pubs and clubs and other safer and cleaner places to meet partners? My research suggests three main reasons:

1. You don't have to make any commitment. If you're deeply in the closet, but hanker for gay sex, then a cottage is the place you can get it without having to enter into gay culture. Most of the cottaging cases that appear in the local papers seem to concern married men – the sort of people who wouldn't visit a gay club if it was the last place on earth.

2. You don't have to be young, beautiful and charming to get sex in a cottage, whereas in a gay club or pub the older and less hunky tend to lose out (although a survey by the London Gay Teenage Group reported that 40 per cent of the young men questioned said they had had sex in a cottage).

3. Some men enjoy the extra thrill provided by the risk of discovery. Some have told me that they have come to find the smell of lavatories quite erotic, and gain some perverse pleasure from the disgusting surroundings.

The police, of course, stake out the better patronised cottages on a regular basis and often make mass arrests. Some cottagers are well organised in this respect and post lookouts during the action.

Perhaps one of the most open and unrepentant cottagers was the playwright Joe Orton. In his diaries he glorifies and extols his casual sexual encounters. An entry in 1966 describes in lyrical detail one such encounter in North London. It is included here for the edification of those who have never cottaged and do not know what goes on, and because it is one of the few documentary accounts of a fairly common occupation in this country:

"When I left I took the Piccadilly line to Holloway Road and popped into a little pissoir – just four pissers. It was dark because someone had taken the bulb away. There were three figures pissing. I had a piss, and as my eyes became used to the gloom, I saw that only one of the figures was worth having – a labouring type, big with cropped hair and, as far as I could see, wearing jeans and a dark short coat. Another man entered and the man next to the labourer moved away, not out of the place altogether, but back against the wall. The new man had a pee and left the place and, before the man against the wall could return to his place, I nipped in there sharpish and stood next to the labourer. I put my hand down and felt his cock, he immediately started to play with mine. The youngish man with fair hair, standing back against the wall, went into the vacant place. I unbuttoned the top of my jeans and unloosened my belt in order to allow the labourer free rein with my balls. The man next to me began to feel my bum. At this point a fifth man entered. Nobody moved. It was dark. Just a little light spilled into the place from the street, not enough to see immediately. The man next to me moved back to allow the fifth man to piss. But the fifth man very quickly flashed his cock and the man next to me returned to my side, lifting up my coat and shoving his hand down the back of my trousers. The fifth man kept puffing on a cigarette end and, by the glowing end, watched. A sixth man came into the pissoir. As it was so dark nobody bothered to move. After an interval (during which the fifth man watched me feel the labourer, the labourer stroked my cock, and the man besides me pulled my jeans down even further), I noticed that the sixth man was kneeling down beside the youngish man with fair hair and sucking his cock. A seventh man came in, but by now nobody cared. The number of people in the place was so large that detection was impossible. And anyway, as soon became apparent when the seventh man stuck his head down on a level with my fly, he wanted a cock in his mouth too. For some moments nothing happened. The eighth man, bearded and stocky, came in. He pushed the sixth man roughly away from the fair-haired man and quickly sucked the fair-haired man off. The man beside me had pulled my jeans down over my buttocks and was trying to push his prick between my legs. The fair-haired man, having been sucked off, hastily left the place. The bearded man came over and nudged away the seventh man from me and, opening wide my fly, began sucking me like a maniac. The labourer, getting very excited by my feeling his cock with both hands, suddenly glued his mouth to mine. The little pissoir under the bridge had become the scene of a frenzied homosexual saturnalia. No more than two feet away the citizens of Holloway moved about their ordinary business. I came, squirting come into the bearded man's mouth and pulled up my jeans. As I was about to leave, I heard the bearded man hissing quietly, 'I suck people off! Who wants his cock sucked?' When I left, the labourer was just shoving his cock into the man's mouth to keep him quiet. I caught the bus home"

Efforts to stop cottagers using public loos are ongoing; some employ attendants to ensure that no-one lingers, and some lavatories have very small doors on the cubicles so that minimum privacy is afforded. One old cottage habitué told me how he would always carry a large shopping bag with him when cottaging. If he was lucky, he would take his partner into a lavatory stall and one of them would stand in the shopping bag. If anyone was glancing under the shortened door to see how many occupants were in the cubicle, all they would see would be one pair of feet and a shopping bag.

Cottages are smelly and dangerous, but they are also havens for those who just want sex and a little bit of companionship.

The American researcher Laud Humphreys did a large-scale study of cottagers (published as *Tearoom Trade*) and came to the conclusion that lavatories often attract those men who are looking for sex which is non-committed, but more companionable than masturbation. He found that many straight men resorted to cottages when sex with their wives had stopped.

Crabs

See pubic lice for full details of these common little horrors.

Crotch

'Crutch' 'basket' or 'packet' are other charming euphemisms for the crotch-area. To say that someone has a 'bulging basket' indicates that either they are well hung or that they've quietly slipped a liverwurst into their undies. Baskets can become an obsession with some gay men, but there is nothing judgmental about such a statement. The appreciation of baskets is one of life's great pleasures, and has its equivalent with the love of fine food. Sometimes a meal is indifferent, but sometimes it is inspired. And so it is with basket-study – some deserve only the merest glance, while others call for prolonged and minute inspection, with each contour and protuberance being given proper attention.

It is a pleasant coincidence that most men like to sit with their legs spread well apart – sometimes at a contorted angle of almost 90 degrees – unconsciously inviting us to view what they have to offer. This display, when coupled with tight trousers, can provide hours of harmless speculative entertainment during a long tube or bus journey. The trick is to try and not make your observations too obvious. However bulging a basket may be, don't stare at its interesting undulations too intently or your research might result in your receiving a smack in the mouth from some spoilsport straight.

Your own crotch can be made interesting for others to view if you sand paper your jeans to paper thinness in that area. The wearing of chaps – those leather trousers with the crotch cut out, much beloved of cowboys – can give extra emphasis to any particularly prominent feature you may wish to exhibit.

Do not be tempted to stuff foreign objects into your pants with the intention of misleading potential partners. Once the keks come off, there might be some explaining to do if a carefully cut length of hose pipe suddenly unfurls from your undies.

CRUISING

Cruising, as searching for sex in public is called, can be done almost anywhere, but isolated woodlands, graveyards and parklands are favourite locations – as are cottages and their environs. In big cities there are sometimes streets which become famous for cruising. Piccadilly Circus was once the hub of cruising in central London, as was Charing Cross. A guide book to London published in 1855 (*The Yokel's Preceptor or More Sprees In London*), commented on the proliferation of male prostitutes – described as '*margeries* or *pooffs*' – walking the streets. The author informed readers that in bars around Charing Cross could be seen notices warning "Beware of Sods". He then revealed how to recognise the said 'pooffs': "They generally congregate around the picture shops, and are to be known by their effeminate air, their fashionable dress &c. When they see what they imagine to be a chance, they place their fingers in a peculiar manner underneath the tails of their coat, and wag them about – their method of giving the office."

In 1808, Lord Hawkesbury, the then Home Secretary, wrote that "many persons had been found lately, loitering about St James's (and Hyde) Park(s) every evening after dark who are known to have unnatural propensities; and to meet there for the purpose of making assignations with each other."

Parisian police records show that similar trolling was going on in the Tuileries and the Luxembourg gardens, where the convention was to approach a likely partner with a request for tobacco.

These days, cruising can also be done more safely in gay pubs. Some pubs specialise in a meat-rack approach, where dim lights, heavy music and a smoky atmosphere create a sexual charge in the air. The sole purpose of these bars (if you discount the sale of alcohol) is to pick up partners, so nobody tries to pretend otherwise. Often you will see men lined up against a wall waiting for an approach. These bars can seem sinister and unwelcoming to the newcomer. Smiling is not encouraged and everyone seems to be doing their best to look threatening and macho – a posture known in the USA as 'attitude'.

In the USA cruising in cars along the long, wide boulevards of LA (especially Sunset Strip) is a popular pastime for those in search of male hustlers.

For successful street cruising, follow these simple guidelines. As you walk along the street, and you see someone walking towards you who you'd like to get to know better, wait until you're about five feet apart and then look directly into his eyes (the eye-lock, as it is known). If he holds your gaze for a fraction of a second longer than is usual between strangers, walk by and then look back over your shoulder. If he is similarly looking back to see what *your* reaction is, then you can then turn round and approach him with a non-committal question such as: "Do you have a light?" or "Can you tell me where such and such a street is?" Body language and facial expression will tell you quite clearly whether he is interested in further intercourse or whether you have misread the situation.

Cuddles

What is it that men find most satisfying about the sexual encounters they have with one another? According to one large-scale survey carried out by Shere Hite (published as *The Hite Report on Male Sexuality*) many men found that cuddling was by far the most satisfying thing about their contact with each other. They loved the skin to skin contact, the stroking and the hugging. One man even said that he would be completely happy if he could spend the whole night with his lover laying in his arms, with no heavy sex play at all.

The feel of men is very different to that of women: their strength, the coarseness and hairiness of their skin; the roughness of their hands. They smell different and taste different, and this is the very essence of what gay men find attractive about each other. Cuddling and embracing is one way to get close to, and maybe even yielding to the strength and power that many men's bodies exude. Being enveloped by a pair of brawny arms and held close to a well-developed chest is a thrill beyond compare. Cuddles are one of the great pleasures of a gay sexual encounter.

Cum

Cum, cream, come, gism, goo, jam, juice, load, love juice, man oil, water of life, whipped cream, spunk or ejaculate is the mixture of sperm and seminal fluid which constitutes semen, that delightful sticky stuff that squirts out of the penis during orgasm.

Cum has an interesting history before it even sees the light of day. The sperms are made inside tiny tubes which are coiled up inside the testicles. From there they are transferred to the epididymis, which is a sort of storage area attached to the back of the testes. Here they spend about six weeks ripening before moving on through a tube called the vas deferens, to another set of storage compartments called the ampulla.

Just at the lower end of the ampulla, the vas deferens connects to the seminal vesicles, where seminal fluid is manufactured. When seminal fluid and sperms mix together – with a little extra ingredient supplied by the prostate gland – it makes semen, or cum to you and me.

Just like Coca Cola, no-one knows the exact formula for this delightful cocktail, but unlike Coca Cola, the flavour and texture varies from one batch to the next. As those who enjoy the taste of cum will testify, it can range from almost sweet to almost salty, from the watery to the glutinous.

Cum, unfortunately, is an excellent transporter of HIV, and so it is important that we take every precaution we can think of to stop other people's semen getting into our body. We can do this easily by the employment of condoms, which act as a barrier while still allowing us to be thoroughly filthy.

It's no good thinking you can dispense with condoms because you imagine it is safe to pull your cock out of his arse just before you shoot your load; a substance called pre-cum (q.v.) can leak out of the penis before the main load is discharged, and this too can be infected with HIV. So, use a condom before you go in and keep it on until you come out.

Many men enjoy having their partner shoot their load over them, either on their face or some other part of the body – so they can rub the semen over their skin. This is fine as long as there are no cuts or scratches in the area where the semen is being smeared.

Cum has an extraordinary ability to get into places where other fluids cannot reach, and even though we shoot only about half a teaspoonful at a time, it can feel like pints when it gets on the bed sheets. Many a relationship has been strained by arguments about who is going to sleep on the wet patch.

Cum can also wreak havoc on deep-pile carpets where it goes hard, crusty and matted. And we've all heard the one about the young man who wanked so much at night that he fell downstairs and broke his pyjamas.

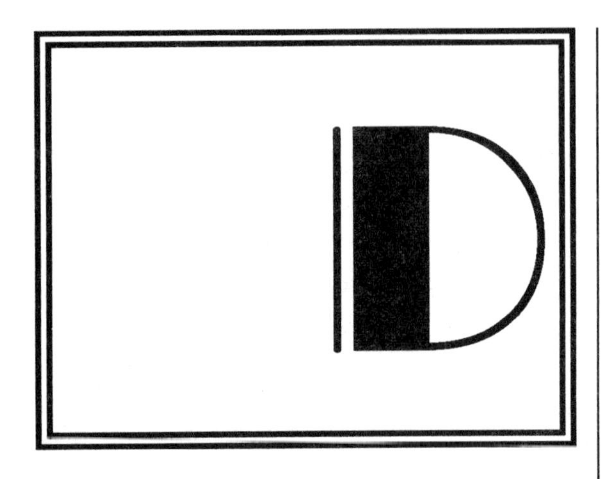

Daisy chain

Group sex in which all the participants are joined together in a long line of activity. They may all be doing the same thing to each other or it may be a succession of variations. First man being fellated, the fellator is being fucked (hopefully using a condom), while the fucker is rimming (q.v.) a fourth, who in turn is fellating someone else and so on. In the USA this is also known as a "floral arrangement".

Dental dams

These small devices are also called oral shields and should be used as a safer sex precaution during rimming. You can find them for sale in the gay press small ads. If you can't find one when you need it, you could use a double layer of cling-film as an alternative (try to find the type that contains no toxins). Use each dental dam only once and then discard it. Before use, wash away any powder or lint that may be clinging to the dam and then let it dry, or dry it with a clean towel. Place the dam over the anal opening, and then rim away to your tongue's content.

Don't try to use other types of plastic material, such as dustbin bags, as these often contain toxic substances.

Dental dams will give some protection from possible HIV infection and hepatitis A and B.

Depravity

Most of us have fantasies in which we dream of unfettered sexual 'depravity'. In these dirty day-dreams we can conjure up men who are prepared to gratify our every sick fancy, and never demand anything for themselves. If only we could find such a creature in real life. But that's just for fun, and to my mind nothing is really depraved unless it involves real violence, cruelty or exploitation. Genuine depravity is revolting. I once saw some photographs of a gay man in Iran being stoned to death. I felt sick for weeks afterwards. The ayatollahs say he deserved his fate for being wicked and depraved. But which is the real depravity here?

Desire

Where does desire come from – our heads, our hearts or our crotch? What makes us want to have sex with some people and not with others? We know that when we are making a breakthrough with a potential new sex partner there can be a delicious tingle between our legs. Does this emanate from our brain, which is telling us that we're likely to have a good time with this person? Or does that tingle in our bollocks send a message to our brain to tell it to make us charming, desirable and to do the right things in order to get what we want in the way of jollies?

It has been said that the brain is the most potent sex organ that we have ('The mind is an erogenous zone' as Marilyn Monroe put it). Desire comes from our accumulated experiences, and the knowledge of what feels good. All this information and preference is stored in our brain. Desire then, is an emotional reaction first and a physical reaction second – although it often seems like the other way round. We've heard it said that some men are led by their cock, but that is just a phallusy.

From the Italian *diletto* meaning 'delight', the dildo is an ancient idea, but all the best ones are. A phallus-shaped sex toy with which to pleasure yourself when the real thing isn't available, or simply as an additional thrill. Makeshift dildoes have been improvised from all sorts of items – from bottles to vegetables, from broom-handles to candles. Nowadays they are manufactured from rubber and moulded from actual penises for maximum realism – veins, foreskins, the lot. They can be plain or fancy, simple or elaborate. They can vibrate, shoot "cum", and be double-headed so that two people can use them at the same time. Dildoes can be great fun, and the only real danger might come from using one that was too big. Avoid any that are longer than ten inches or have sharp edges that could splinter or scratch. Ensure that there is a a handle or rope at the end so that you can keep a secure hold of it once you've shoved it in. Many an embarrassing visit has been made to hospital casualty departments by men whose arses have swallowed up their dildo - or carrot or coke bottle or whatever other instrument they've been using to pleasure themselves.

If you do lose your dildo up there, don't hang about, seek medical assistance. Hospital emergency rooms see more cases of this particular dilemma than you'd imagine.

From a safer sex point of view, it's wise not to use other people's dildoes or vibrators. If you are sharing it with someone, make sure it is well washed – disinfected even, in one part bleach to ten parts water – before you insert it into yourself. Alternatively, or even additionally, cover it with a condom.

If someone wants you to fuck them with a dildo – or you have a hankering to be fucked by one – take care not to be too rough. It's easy to cause damage inside the anus, so lubricate it well and slide it in and out gently, without twisting at angles. Listen to what you partner is telling you, and stop immediately if he protests or is in pain. (See also Sex Toys)

Dirty sex

Some gay men like the idea of dirty sex, the kind that involves unwashed bodies, smelly crevices and disgusting surroundings. They get an erotic buzz from having it away in dark alleys among the dustbins or in stinking cottages where the smell of piss is all-pervading. They like the idea of uninhibited wallowing in unsavoury places with unhygienic partners. Often they want their partners to piss or shit on them. They want to push their noses into unwiped bottoms and suck cock that smells like ripe camembert. William Burroughs eat your heart out.

Why, you might ask, would anyone want to do that? Perhaps it's just acting out their feelings that homosexuality itself is dirty. As with any fetish, the urge to have dirty sex can be most pressing for those who crave it.

There is an ever-present possibility of disease for someone who frequently seeks out this kind of sex, but often the urge is so deeply felt that other considerations go by the board.

However, we must not forget the immortal words of Woody Allen on this topic: "Sex is only dirty if you're doing it right."

Disability

Those with a physical disability often complain that at worst their sexuality is ignored or denied and at best it is patronised. Depending on the nature and extent of the disability, there can be problems in getting out and about to find the kinds of partners you might want. Those who need to use wheelchairs, for instance, are often excluded from gay events simply because they can't gain access to the venues. Those who have tried will tell tales of being unwelcome and being treated as a nuisance or, worse still, a coat rack.

Wheelchair users are often seen as little more than an extension of the machine itself. For those with severely restricted mobility, therefore, actually finding sex in the first place may be a vast problem. If you are dependent on other people in order to get around, then it may be doubly difficult. The "carer" may be anti-gay or be unconvinced that their charge's sexual needs exist, far less being important.

However, some gay people with disabilities are persistent. They refuse to let anything stop them. They find friends in other ways – by advertising in the papers or electronic bulletin boards, by going to friendly groups who will provide access for them and so on.

Even for those who manage to find a sexual partner, there may be restrictions on the type of sex they can have. Those paralysed from the waist down, for instance, may be unable to manage any kind of genital sex for themselves, but that does not mean that their sexual needs are non-existent. I have a paraplegic friend who has no feeling in his crotch, but who longs for human contact, loving communication and horny sex. He has succeeded in making contacts through advertising in the gay press, and has found several people who are prepared to share their bodies with him.

He is an intelligent man and it is impossible to patronise him. He is great fun to be with, and he tells me he gives a great blow-job and hand-relief. He also enjoys having his tits sucked and played with – the nerves to this area of his body are fully functioning and he makes full use of them.

Other people who have been recently diagnosed with some illness which they feel is going to end their sex life are often given dud advice by doctors. Multiple sclerosis, diabetes and other conditions which can interfere with the functioning of the sexual equipment don't necessarily mean that sex is forbidden. Don't take your doctor's prognostications as the last word – find a therapist who might be able to help you see a light at the end of the tunnel. Men who have recently discovered that they are seriously ill will probably be suffering from depression and shock, and so there is little wonder that their approach to sex – and probably most other things – has changed. Erection failure for some might not be due to their 'condition' but to the psychological pressure that goes with it.

Sex for people who have recently become disabled may be a matter of rethinking. What we thought was our ideal way of having sex may no longer be an option, but that does not mean that *all* options are closed. As Dr. Bernard Zilbergeld puts it: "Are we saying then that regardless of your physical condition you have the capacity to function sexually as you once did or as a man in very good health can? In truth, we aren't sure. Some men have been able to do so. For others, however, it wasn't the way it used to be. But the way it used to be isn't the only way to be sexual."

Those people with severe learning difficulties are a different matter. Although their sexual needs may be just as developed and pressing as anyone else's, they are seen by the law as exploitable and in need of protection. It is illegal, under the Mental Health Act, to have sex with someone whom the court adjudges to be incapable of giving informed consent.

Groups to contact:

- Regard, a national disabled lesbian and gay organisation. Write to BM Regard, London WC1N 3XX.
- Gay Men's Disabled Group, c/o Manchester Gay Centre, PO Box 153, Manchester M60 1LP.

- Lesbian and Gay Disability Group, c/o Trevor Sword, 16 Gingle Close, Bourneville, Birmingham B30 1RB. Tel: 0121-459 5859.
- Visually Impaired Gay Group. Call Keith on 01705 524739 before 10pm weekdays.
- Deaf Lesbian and Gay Group, c/o 7 Victoria Avenue, South Croydon, Surrey CR2 0QP. Tel: 0181-660 2208 (minicom, eves only).

(i). sexual

Sexual disasters can't always be avoided; they're likely to happen to any of us. You can't be at your best all the time, and sex isn't always the wonderful, carefree experience we'd like it to be. Sometimes things go wrong (such as you get agonising cramp in your leg just as your partner is about to climax); sometimes they never really get going in the first place (such as when you realise that, just as you've got into bed, you've made a terrible mistake and that don't fancy this person in the least).

Typical disasters include:

- Repeatedly trying to penetrate a partner, failing miserably and having to give up (this sometimes leads to the abandonment of the whole proceeding).

- Leaving the KY tube on the bed with the top off and then rolling over on it (the bed can become intolerable for a while after that).

- Ejaculating on to the bedclothes also means that someone is going to have to sleep on the wet patch, which is far from pleasant on a winter night. A handy supply of towels or kitchen roll can help with this if you do not want to make the semen part of your love play (some people like to lick it off their partner's face or body, or massage it in).

I have often heard of people anxious to make a big impression on an attractive stranger, only to be let down by that very anxiety. We all know someone who, when they're nervous, starts talking and doesn't seem able to stop. Or the ones who want to say something, but become tongue-tied and monosyllabic.

Who hasn't tried to spend a romantic night wrapped in the arms of a hunk only to find that, in the wee small hours of the morning, their arm has gone dead necessitating a rapid disturbance of the romantic position in order to forestall the onset of gangrene? Who hasn't involuntarily gagged during oral sex or not had their chopper painfully scratched by jagged teeth?

Accidental farts or belches can also take the shine off that romantic image of yourself which you've been carefully cultivating all night. Go steady on the beer if you also want to avoid the dreaded "no show", or brewer's droop, when peter simply won't rise to the occasion.

Over-excitement can also lead to "premature ejaculation" – you shoot your load almost as soon as you've got your pants down.

Energetic sexual activity can sometimes result in painfully bumped heads, falling out of bed, accidental kneeing of private parts, strained necks, poked eyes and unintentional tickling. Laughter can take the tension out of such mishaps, but sometimes laughter – when it is unexplained – can feel like humiliation to the person who is not in on the joke. This is followed by a rapid loss of interest. Some people are extremely sensitive to "jokes" made during sex. Don't risk it until you are certain your partner trusts you enough to realise that you aren't taunting him.

I've heard tales of people who have had inadequately wiped arses offered to them for rimming. How does one tell a grown man, without somewhat spoiling the erotic atmosphere, that he needs lessons in toilet paper usage?

Sex is such a complicated business that the possibilities of cock-ups (or, perhaps, cock-downs) are almost limitless.

Experienced lovers recognise that they can't get it right every time and shrug off the occasional mistake or disaster. Those who aren't so well experienced can be traumatised and feel humiliated when they make erotic errors and in some cases it can lead to problems. (See Impotence). But being able to smile when things go wrong and forgive each other for being clumsy or tired or whatever the problem is, is the sign of a mature lover.

Disasters (ii) literary

C. K. Scott-Moncrieff translated gay novelist Marcel Proust's epic work *A la recherché du temps perdu* from French into English. The problem was that hoity-toity Moncrieff (who was also gay) didn't understand the smutty bits. For instance, he failed to realise that *casser le pot* is French slang meaning to bugger. He translated the phrase literally (to break the pot), making the rest of the passage totally incomprehensible. A new translation has put right these howlers.

Docking

This is an interesting one, only possible for an individual with a foreskin which is much longer and more voluminous than average. He can then invite his partner to insert his cock under the foreskin of his own cock (thus 'docking', as in shipping or spacecraft). They can then wank together. There is a small risk of HIV infection if the spunk from an infected person gets into the cock of another.

Doggy fashion

This is one of the most popular – if not *the* most popular – positions for enjoying a man-to-man fuck. The receptor kneels down on all fours and his partner approaches from behind. This position allows quite deep penetration, particularly if the passive partner kneels with his legs spread apart, and then puts his face on the floor so that his arse is pushed up with the cheeks well spread.

The person in the driving seat is totally unfettered and has complete freedom to thrust. He can do this on his knees, from a squatting position or draped over his partner's back, nibbling his ears. The only disadvantage of doing it doggy-style is that it is difficult to kiss each other unless you can twist your neck round, *Exorcist*-style, quite a long way. There might also be a problem for the bottom man's knees if the session goes on for any length of time. Most people are happy to put up with this minor inconvenience for the sheer pleasure of the total experience.

It is possible to utilise mirrors, too. If it is important for you to see your partner's face, or if you want to see other parts of the action that are difficult to manage when you're in this particular position.

Always use a condom when penetrative sex is involved. Remember that anal sex is by far the most effective means of transmitting HIV.

Domination & Submission

The question of domination is very important in all kinds of sex; some people find that dominating, or being dominated, is extremely exciting. Domination plays an essential role in fantasy as well as in SM scenes.

Domination can take many forms, from one partner "forcing" his partner to abide by his wishes, to full-scale corporal punishment and humiliation. Ritual domination and submission scenes can become a way of life for some people, and elaborate signal codes are created by those who are skilled in this sort of sex to ensure that it is only symbolic and that the dominated partner can call an end to the proceedings whenever it's getting out of hand. (See also Sado-Masochism).

Double-rub

A very pleasant activity, a variation on mutual masturbation. The two partners stand very close together, facing each other. One grabs both cocks in one hand (or both hands if they're particularly thick) and wanks them simultaneously. This is most successful if the cocks are approximately the same length. There is a slight chance of HIV transmission if you climax in this position, as semen from one partner might get into the cock of the other. Condoms, again, can solve that one.

Drag

Drag used to mean dressing up in clothes of the opposite sex, but now it means wearing any kind of clothing to create an effect. Therefore, men who dress up in full motor-cycling gear (even though they don't own a bike) are just as much in drag as those who flounce around in chiffon and lurex dresses.

Soldiers, building-site workers, cowboys and other uniformed icons can be seen strutting around the gay scene. Few of them are genuine – most are just dragged up.

Cross-dressing has always been a popular pastime for some gay men, and I know one gentleman who likes being fucked while dressed as Grace Kelly. His fantasy is of some hefty man pulling up his dress, ripping down his knickers and violating "Princess Grace" in the most disgusting fashion – by fucking her up the arse. He gets more men than you would imagine to go along with this little scene.

Theatrical drag goes back a long way – as far as the thirteenth century, in fact, when the church forbade women to appear on stage. When that ban was lifted, drag went into a decline until Victorian times when pantomime dames were invented, and then it made a return in a big way. Nowadays some of our top comedians are men in frocks, and the British seem to have an inordinate fondness for them. There is something deeply significant about a country that is so hung up about sex, liking to see its men dress up as 'ladies'.

Perhaps the best comment about drag was from Tallulah Bankhead, who was attending a ceremony at St Patrick's, the big Catholic cathedral in New York. As the priest walked by, in his full jewel-encrusted regalia, swinging his smoking incense-burner, she said: "Darling, I love the drag, but your handbag's on fire!" (see also Transvestism)

Drugs

Illegal drugs aren't hard to come by on the gay scene – or anywhere else, if you look hard enough – and it has become fashionable to drop a little E or snort a little coke in order to keep going through these long nights. The occasional indulgence is probably OK, but once you get into the routine of taking these stimulants to keep you awake and "give you energy" you can easily find yourself on the slippery slope to dependence. You know more than most, I expect, the dangers of shooting up with shared needles. I can only say, don't do it, but if you're addicted (and you always said you would never become addicted), these are empty words. If you haven't started yet, don't get started. Drugs can't solve any problems, they can only create them. For every Ecstasy-induced high, there will be a thousand lows. Leave drugs alone and work on the problems that are really pestering you.

Poppers – amyl- or butyl- nitrate – are also popular, and aren't illegal at the moment. Originally developed for people with heart complaints like angina, the substances come in a small glass phial which can be "popped" open and sniffed when the attack is coming on. The effect is to dilate the blood vessels and cause a rush of blood to the head. A short-lived feeling of euphoria is created and consequently poppers are often sniffed at the moment of orgasm. There is some controversy over the desirability of using poppers over any length of time and certainly they should be avoided by people with heart or kidney conditions. Some people insist that they are perfectly harmless if used properly, while others suspect that their continued use over long periods might compromise the immune system. You pays your money and you takes your chance.

Group to contact:

- Blenheim Project - counselling for drug users - 0181-960 5599 (Mon-Fri 10am-5pm)
- Narcotics Anonymous lesbian and gay group 0171 351 6794

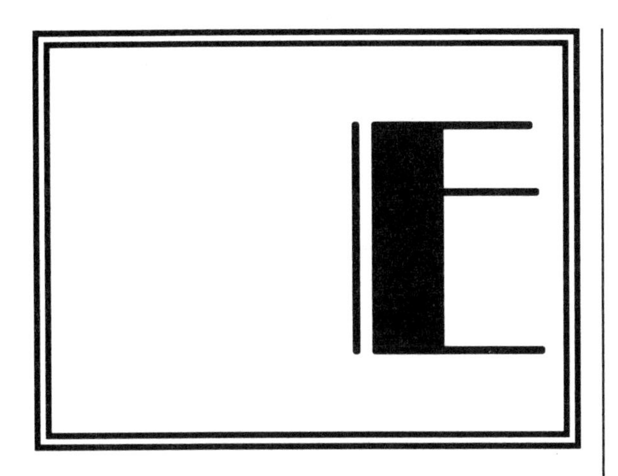

Ecstasy

The word ecstasy is derived from the Greek *existanai* meaning to drive out of one's senses. Sexual ecstasy is available to anyone who is prepared to let themselves go and let it happen. Ecstasy the drug is available to anyone prepared to pay the price and take the risks. Ecstasy or simply 'E' is becoming more and more prevalent on the gay scene, and is very popular because it gives a burst of energy and a feeling of euphoria that can keep the user dancing and loving through the night. There is, of course, a price to be paid. When you get high on alcohol you know you are going to feel lousy in the morning and Ecstasy is likely to have a similar effect. The more you take and worse it gets. So, if you're tempted to try Ecstasy, don't do it too often – give your body a chance to recuperate before you go again. Don't take more than one tablet. And don't drink alcohol in combination with E, it will simply dehydrate you; stick to water and fruit juices, and plenty of it. Eat a good meal before you go out as Ecstasy is likely to depress your appetite, and frequent use can lead to dramatic weight loss.

If you use Ecstasy on a regular basis, it can affect your attitude to life. Although it is not addictive physically, it can be very seductive emotionally and it is easy to become dependent on it as a prop to get you through a busy social whirl. It can also eat up your money – at twenty quid a throw, it ain't cheap.

Ecstasy is a category "A" drug, which makes it the same as Heroin as far as the law is concerned. Possession can result in a large fine, not to mention the criminal record, and supplying to other people might even result in a jail sentence.

Effeminate

Effeminate comes from the Latin 'to become like a woman' and is defined in the Oxford English Dictionary as: 'womanish, unmanly, enervated, feeble, self-indulgent, voluptuous, unbecomingly delicate, or over-refined.' These are all loaded and judgmental terms – what's wrong with being like a woman? There's nothing wrong with women!

All the same, effeminacy is a big issue in the gay community. Just look at the personal ads in almost any gay magazine and you'll find them peppered with phrases like "non-camp" or "straight-acting" or "no femmes need apply". What is it that so many gay men find so threatening about their effeminate brethren? Is it that femmes remind them, rather bluntly, about their own sexual preferences? Is it that men who love men simply don't fancy men who behave like women?

It is not like this in other cultures. Indeed, only by adopting effeminate mannerisms in some countries will a gay man be able to openly pursue his chosen lifestyle. In Tahiti, there is a sort of "third sex" – men who assume feminine characteristics and who are accepted, and even, according to anthropologists, granted a "semi-institutionalised position of esteem." The North American Indians, too, had a class of men called *berdache* who usually had sex with other males of the tribe, though not with other male *berdache*. Often they 'married' male braves, forming stable and long-term unions which frequently lasted until the death of a partner.

Not everyone is put off sex with effeminate men, and some even seek out transvestites as partners. The recent furore over the activities of North African trannies who were using the Bois de Bolougne in Paris as an outdoor brothel revealed that there is no shortage of customers for the services they offer.

EJACULATION

Ejaculation is what happens during orgasm, when semen is pumped out of the penis. The process of shooting one's load is governed by the "sympathetic nervous system", that part of our body's mechanism over which we have no conscious control. Once the orgasm has begun there is no stopping it, all we can do is lay back and enjoy it. Our only control is over the timing of the ejaculation – we can stop and start stimulation at crucial moments until we are ready for the finale.

Men ejaculate in three spurts: first from the Cowper's glands, then the prostate, then the testicles. We usually produce something like half a teaspoonful of semen (4 cubic centimetres with a weight of 4 grams) at each ejaculation, which contains an average of 300 million sperms. The first shot travels up the penis at an average of 28 miles an hour. Fascinating, isn't it?

A full erection is not an absolute necessity in order to ejaculate. Most of us have, at some time, woken up with a steaming hard-on and begun to work towards an orgasm, only to find that the penis starts to deflate before we've got there. If we persist, however, most of us have managed to bring it off even with a less-than-rigid cock. The ejaculation is more likely to be a dribble than a spurt in such circumstances. However, an orgasm with a totally flaccid cock is a rarity indeed.

Some men worry that they can't produce a dramatic fountain of spunk when they ejaculate. They imagine that something is wrong with them because it just sort of meanders out rather than shooting right across the room. However, our fire-power is an individual characteristic and has nothing to do with being normal or abnormal. Just as some men have stronger biceps, so some men have stronger ejaculatory muscles. Whether your ejaculation is like a cruise missile emerging from a rocket launcher or more a stream of lava running down the side of a volcano, the accompanying sensations are much the same for everyone.

The commonest sexual problem for men is that of premature ejaculation – or 'coming' too soon. It seems that no sooner have you started, than it's all over. Sometimes it's a product of inexperience and tension, sometimes just over-excitement. It might be the result of having sex after a long period of abstinence. It nearly always happens with a partner and hardly ever during solo sex.

But wait – let's not create problems where there may be none. Premature ejaculation is a term that is falling out of favour with sexologists because much depends on the definition of "premature". Some men find it quite satisfactory if they come after just a few thrusts, or a couple of minutes after direct genital stimulation has begun. Most men would consider that they had done well if they could keep thrusting for five or ten minutes without coming. There is only a problem if you find yourself frustrated and unable to exercise any control over your ejaculation (say, for instance, you were to shoot your load at your lover's first touch, leaving both of you annoyed that no real sexual exploration had taken place).

If premature ejaculation is a problem for you, then the order of the day is: don't panic. There are ways of training yourself not to come too soon. During your masturbation sessions is a good time to put things right. Just wank away, but when you feel the orgasm approaching, squeeze the end of your penis between your thumb and forefinger quite hard. This will cause the orgasmic process to stop and maybe some of the erection to be lost. After the sensation has passed, start again and repeat the process as many times as you can manage without coming. This will have the effect of training your body not to shoot too soon after your cock is touched. If you have a partner, you can get him to do this for you. Ask him to stimulate you, but then let him know when the orgasm is approaching (but before it's inevitable) and get him to put the squeeze on (he should squeeze the head of the penis, where the glans meets the shaft, between his thumb and forefinger). He should repeat this as many times as possible before you come. After a few sessions of this, you will find that you will be gaining more control.

The opposite of premature ejaculation is "retarded ejaculation". This means that however much stimulation you get, you just can't bring it off. It happens to all of us from time to time and is usually a self-correcting problem, brought on by nerves. If the problem persists over a long period, though, medical help should be sought.

Ellis, Havelock

Havelock Ellis was a Victorian sexologist who first proposed the idea that, for some people, homosexuality is an inborn characteristic. The first volume of his work *Studies in the Psychology of Sex* published in 1897, was entitled "Sexual Inversion".

Until that time it was thought that anybody who "indulged" in homosexual acts was simply making a "moral choice" to behave wickedly (as they might make a moral choice to steal). Such people Ellis termed "perverts". But people who he considered were constitutionally attracted to members of their own sex were termed "inverts" and were regarded as sick rather than evil. ("Sexual inversion as here understood," he wrote, "means sexual instinct turned by inborn constitutional abnormality towards persons of the same sex.")

Although Ellis's ideas have been superseded and contradicted by those who came after (particularly by Freud, who considered homosexuality to be the result of a defective upbringing), they did create the concept of "homosexual people", which had previously been untenable.

Endowed (Well)

In our phallocentric culture there is a sense of awe and wonder at the sight of a really big cock. We still cling, however subliminally, to the idea that being well-endowed gives a man sexual abilities that are denied to others.

The longest human cock on record measured thirteen inches, although doubtless, somewhere out there, unmeasured, are bigger ones. But possessing a monster tool does not necessarily guarantee the ability to use it properly. It has been said over and over again that imagination is the *real* sex organ, but that does not dampen the primitive lust which is generated by the sight of A Man Called Horse.

Things have not always been so. In ancient Athens a big cock was thought of as hilarious, and in Greek art and drama much fun was made of large pudenda. On that basis, Jeff Stryker would have made a fortune as a stand-up comedian in the amphitheatre. The preferred size in classical times was small and delicate. The playwright Aristophenes was given to using the word *posthion* – "little prick" – as a term of endearment. Young athletes in Athens even went so far as to tie their cocks between their legs with a leather string in an effort to make them look small.

There are now organisations for men who consider themselves to be "too small" (Peanuts Clubs, they're called) and for those who consider themselves "too large" (yes, some men consider it to be a problem: they complain that people aren't interested in them as whole people, but only in their cocks).

The enema – and its euphemistic variation "colonic irrigation" – started out as a medical procedure, to clear faecal matter out of the bowel and colon in preparation for surgery. A tube is inserted into the anus and warm, sometimes soapy, water is pumped in. This stimulates the urge to defecate, and soon you are completely relieved of all waste matter. As those who have had it done in hospital know, it can be a pleasant experience so long as it is done in a relaxed atmosphere and doesn't involve too much stress and apprehension.

The whole procedure and its paraphernalia has become eroticised and people give each other enemas as part of their sexual explorations. The idea gained currency in the gay community that having an enema (or 'douche', as the Americans call it) before anal sex made the whole thing "cleaner". This theory didn't stand up to examination, though, and nowadays it's considered to be positively undesirable to douche before or after anal sex. If you do it before sex, you might damage the lining of your anal canal, making the transmission of HIV more likely, and if you do it afterwards, you might simply end up washing the virus further into the body. Besides which, too much douching can upset the body's natural bacterial balance and cause problems in the bowel.

If giving or receiving enemas is your idea of a sexy time, then save them for those occasions when you won't be combining them with rectal sex. Don't be tempted to use anything other than warm, soapy water – other substances can cause much damage. And don't forget a condom whenever penetration is being considered.

Erection

Also called a hard-on, stiffy or tumescence, erection occurs when the spongy chambers which comprise the penis fill with blood, expand and make the penis erect, and better able to penetrate. The foreskin usually rolls back to expose the glans of the penis, which might also change colour.

Having an erection isn't necessarily the signal that a man wants to have sex. Sometimes it's just the result of a full bladder, and many men wake up in the morning with a hard on, but not necessarily the urge to put it to any use. Conversely not having an erection doesn't necessarily mean that you aren't interested in having sex.

Some men are much quicker to become erect than others, needing only the smallest amount of stimulation in order to get a boner on; others need to be coaxed and cajoled before the member rises. In younger men, only the smallest hint of a promise can be enough to set the procedure in motion. Sometimes vibrations can set it off, too, as on buses and aeroplanes. I remember once travelling on an Intercity train, where a man slumped in the seat opposite had fallen asleep. I don't know what he was dreaming about, but a large, mobile protuberance appeared in the crotch area of his trousers. I knew he must either have a hard-on or be carrying his pet rat in his underpants. He was most embarrassed when he awoke, and lay a raincoat over his lap, hoping that no-one had noticed the little jerking movements that were pushing at his fly.

Sometimes the opposite effect is the cause of embarrassment and humiliation. Erection failure, sometimes called impotence (q.v.), can become a source of great distress for some men. There are many reasons why erections fail to materialise when we most want them. Sometimes it's stress or fears about not being able to perform; it might be nervousness about location. Cottages and woodlands are risky places to have sex, and although they might be exciting to some people, they are so fear-inducing to others that erection becomes impossible.

Erection failure happens to most men at some point in their life. Usually it is a temporary state of affairs that corrects itself with a little patience and understanding. Longer term problems can be helped by therapy.

The sex researchers Masters and Johnson found that some gay men who have a severe, on-going problem with erection failure (or *primary impotence*), may become what they termed "sexual fakers". Because those suffering primary impotence can't achieve an erection, they avoid having to explain the problem by always offering themselves as passive partners in sexual encounters. Their relationships tend to be brief and fleeting because it would be impossible to successfully hide the problem from a longer-term partner. Such is the fear that some men have of being thought "unable to get it up" that it totally controls their sexual options.

The important thing to remember is not to panic if you are going through a period of erection failure. If you allow it to become an obsessive worry, then a vicious circle of fear-filled anticipation followed by the inevitable failure will become established and then be difficult to break.

Sometimes there is a physical reason for impotence. Some drug treatments can cause erection loss, and damaged nerves can also interfere with sexual arousal. If this is a problem for you, don't hesitate to contact your doctor. Don't imagine that he'll be shocked – the problem is so common, he's bound to have come across it before.

In older men, erections are likely to become less firm as time elapses. Some research was done as to the average angle of an erection at different ages. The results were:

- Age 20: 10% above horizontal
- Age 30: 20% above horizontal
- Age 40: Slightly above horizontal
- Age 50: Slightly below horizontal
- Age 70: 25% below horizontal

Erogenous zones

Erogenous zones have been defined by psychologist James L. McCrary as: "those parts of the body possessing a great concentration of nerve ends (sometimes termed 'sexual nerves') that when stimulated, cause sexual arousal".

The most obvious erogenous zones are those on and around our genitals. Having your inner thigh gently brushed by someone's hand can be exquisitely exciting, even if it isn't on its way to your cock. The lips, too, are erogenous, as are buttocks, anus, nipples, under arms – and just about anywhere else.

During sexual excitement our senses – sight, touch, hearing and smell – become much sharper, making us more aware of any stimuli which will intensify our sexual pleasure. The feel of a bristly chin, the touch of an erect penis, the smell of a sweaty orifice or the sight of a face which is ecstatic with lust will all add to the rising pleasure. Parts of the body which would not normally be thought of as sexy can seem intensely sensitive when we are engaged in a sexual encounter. For instance, I have known people who have found that if their partner touches the back of their neck in a non-sexual situation, it is just another touch, but if he touches it during sex play, it becomes an almost unbearably pleasurable sensation.

Lovers should experiment with their own and their partner's erogenous zones. Almost any part of the body can be eroticised.

The feet, the shoulders, the lower back – massage and caress them, and listen for those little sighs and grunts that tell you where your partner likes best to be stroked.

Erotomania

This is a psychiatric condition which afflicts more women than men. It manifests itself when the sufferer becomes sexually obsessed with another person who is usually unattainable or who doesn't reciprocate. Often the sufferer will bombard the object of their love with explicit letters, presents and amorous phone calls. Pop stars and actors are accustomed to being the subject of this particular syndrome, and members of male strip shows and TV's The Gladiators complain constantly that they are harassed by men who have become fixated on them. It can be most uncomfortable and even frightening when an ordinary person becomes the focus of someone else's erotomania.

ESCORT SERVICES

Escort services, the euphemistic title for the hire of rent boys, will provide sexual partners for those who are prepared to pay the sometimes high prices. Naturally rent boys do it for the money, and sometimes they aren't gay. Because it's all operating on the periphery of the law, there is often an element of exploitation and corruption involved, but not always. It's possible, through these services, to meet clean-cut, well-adjusted men who know precisely what they're doing, who are good at their jobs and who can provide company for men who would otherwise be alone. They do it honestly and try to give value for money.

It is, regrettably, also possible to meet thieving little ratbags who think morality is something that doesn't apply to their dealings with gay men. These are the sort of people who will take a client's money and, if there's any more mileage in it, go the Sunday scandal sheets and sell the details to the ever-slavering editors.

Amorality rules in the oldest profession. Journalism, I mean.

EUPHEMISMS

Euphemisms are defined in the O.E.D. as "substitution of mild or vague or roundabout expressions for harsh or blunt or direct ones". Sometimes they can be hilarious, and king of comedy in that respect was surely Thomas Bowdler, a gentleman with so many sexual hang-ups he felt that English literature needed all its "filthy" passages expunged (including talk of mother's milk, virgins and bodily functions). He set about taking all offensive and irreligious references from our sacred texts, including Shakespeare (hence the bowdlerised version, which he entitled *The Family Shakespeare*). His aim in rubbing out the naughty bits was to ensure that they would not raise a blush "on the cheek of modest innocence nor plant a pang in the heart of a devout Christian". In Bowdler's hands Juliet's speech of longing for Romeo was cut from 30 lines to 15. King Lear's speech which begins "Let copulation thrive..." was reduced from 22 lines to seven. He threw out *Othello* completely, declaring it "unfortunately little suited to family reading." Perhaps his most famous euphemism was for "a bull", which he translated as "a gentleman cow."

Because our Victorian forebears (see also under Bigot) didn't like to use the words that were even vaguely connected with sex, we ended up calling the leg and breast of chicken "dark and light meat". In the USA, cockroaches became simply "roaches", and furniture legs were covered up lest they reminded gentlemen of the human variety and inflamed their passions.

Sex has always been a happy hunting ground for euphemisms; gay sex an absolute treasure trove. Because the love that dare not speak its name needed still to communicate, its practitioners had, over the centuries, to think of all kinds of coded ways of saying what they needed to say (see also *polari*). Our enemies, too, who wanted to insult us found new and more offensive ways to do it. A particularly rich source of insulting words for homosexuals can be found in *The Sun*, a pornographic journal addicted to lying, which its owners rather cheekily describe as 'a newspaper'. Most recent of these have been "kharzi cruiser" (kharzi is London slang for lavatory), and "rear gunner".

As Richard Davenport-Hines says in his book *Sex, Death and Punishment* (Faber Press, 1990): "Words are perhaps the most malignant and treacherous of mankind's possessions. They are saturated with all the sorrow and injustice of civilisation. Rich in their potential to enhance the pleasure and meaning of life, they are used often to prevent reflection or understanding, or as instruments of tyranny, or as ruses to separate people from their needs and instincts. The power of words usually results in the destruction rather than the enrichment of individuality. Their power is seldom wielded to achieve human elevation or fulfilment, but more often to deplete lives or eclipse personal experience."

You will find examples of substitute terminology scattered throughout this book, but there follows a list of euphemisms for gay sex and gay people, some of it funny, some of it sickening, some of it antique and no longer in use, some of it having changed meaning, but all of it in need of preservation.

- Aspro (a male prostitute – USA)
- Athenian (a variation on Greek love, q.v.)
- Auntie (an ageing homosexual)
- Arse burglar
- Arse queen (a gay man with a preference for buttocks)
- Australian (term for someone who likes anilingus, e.g. likes kissing "down under")
- Backdoor man
- Backgammoner
- Battyman (West Indian slang for a gay man, probably from *batti* a Jamaican word for buttocks)
- Bender (as in 'one who bends over')
- Bent – (e.g. not straight)
- Bitch
- Bone queen (US slang for someone who likes to suck 'boners' – or erections)
- Booty bandit
- Brown hatter
- Brownie queen
- Bumboy
- Caddie fan (Welch)
- Catamite
- Chicken hawk (gay man who pursues youthful partners)
- Chocolate box poker
- Cissy
- Cocksucker
- Collar and cuff (rhyming slang for puff)
- Cornholer (USA)
- Daisy

- Dirt box snatcher
- Dirt track rider
- Dude
- Dung pusher
- Faggot (fag)
- Fairy
- Flit
- Flower
- Freak
- Fruit (fruitbar, fruitcake)
- Ganymede (from Greek mythology. Ganymede was a Trojan youth whom Zeus made his cup-bearer. As we know, the gods of Olympus were not strictly heterosexual, so it is unclear what the exact duties of a "cup-bearer" might be, but are likely to have involved cock-sucking).
- Gentleman of the backdoor
- Gentleman of the twilight
- Ginger ('ginger beer', cockney rhyming slang for queer).
- Gutfucker
- Haricot (Australian rhyming slang for haricot bean – queen)
- Head-worker
- He-she
- Homo
- Ingler
- Intermediate sex
- Invert
- Iron (Iron hoof – Cockney rhyming slang for 'poof')
- Isosexual
- Jasper
- Jessie
- King Lear (rhyming slang for 'queer')
- Limp-wristed
- Maneater
- Manhole Inspector
- Mary
- Mint
- Musical
- Nancy-boy
- Nelly
- Oscar (after Oscar Wilde. Also 'to Oscarize' – meaning to bugger).
- Pansy
- Pervert
- Poofter (pouf, poof, poove, puff),
- Poo jabber
- Queer
- Queen
- Sausage jockey
- Shirtlifter
- Shitstabber
- Sissy
- Swish
- Theatrical
- *Tourner la page* (French, meaning literally 'page-turner', equivalent of 'shirtlifter')
- Uphill gardener
- Urning (from Urania, goddess of love)
- Vegetarian (a gay man who doesn't like cock-sucking – i.e. a non-meat eater).
- Wanda wandwaver (a gay man who brags about the size of his penis)
- Wooftah

There are a few euphemisms which gay people have applied to their heterosexual brethren, too, the most commonly used being "straight" (from 'straight and narrow' not the opposite of 'bent'). But there is also 'breeders', 'civilians', 'the enemy', 'citizens' (because they have more rights than gays), 'right-handers' and, my personal favourite, 'commoners' (e.g. *not* queens). In fifties America, the vice squad was referred to as 'Lily Law'.

Exhibitionism /Exposure

Some men get a big kick out of showing off to an audience, and the present obsession among younger men with "working out" has made voyeurs of us all. Those men who have spent a lot of time and money getting their body into great shape are unlikely to be shy about putting the results on show, and gay beaches throughout the world are crawling with hunks who wear little, if anything, and are inviting you to look. Modesty is not the name of the game in these circumstances.

We all like to think that people find pleasure in looking at us, which is why we buy clothes which will show us off to what we hope is our best advantage. However, there are some men who get extra thrills from being watched in the act of sex. Some porno stars do it for the money and some do it because they get a kick from knowing that their sexual prowess will be seen and enjoyed by thousands of other men. There are anecdotes in print of elaborate set-ups involving two-way mirrors and peepholes which allow people to watch the bedroom activities of others. The voyeurs imagine that they are the ones getting the illicit thrill, but in fact the whole thing has been arranged by the exhibitionist who is, in fact, using the voyeurs to satisfy his own desire to be watched.

In porn films there is sometimes a third party in the scene who simply watches the action and wanks. This is the person who the viewer is supposed to identify with, and whose place they would like to take.

"Flashing", is a somewhat different matter. It is a rather common urge that some straight men have to expose their genitals to passers-by or to "accidentally" stand starkers at the bedroom window. Flashers generally don't want to have sex with the chosen viewer – they get off on the look of shock and disgust on their victim's face – and this is why they have such a reputation as pathetic little no-accounts who can't do the real thing. Women have found the best approach is to point and giggle. Street flashers are invariably heterosexual, wobbling their bollocks for schoolgirls. Gay men who want to show off can go down the local club and parade around all night in the semi-nude if they want to.

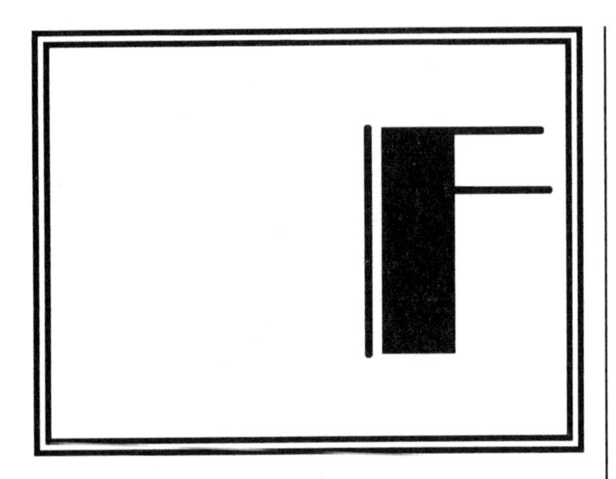

Facial

American euphemism for a getting your cock sucked.

Fantasy

According to Masters and Johnson, "Sexual fantasies begin in childhood and serve important functions in our lives, such as combating boredom, providing or enhancing excitement, releasing inner tensions, and permitting safe, imaginary rehearsals of untried behaviour."

We all have our own virtual reality sex cinema situated inside our heads. It can conjure up anything we want on the fantasy screen, and it is one of the most useful adjuncts to a satisfying sexual life that anyone could have.

Sexual fantasy is such a universal thing that it almost needs no introduction – we've all conjured up images which have excited us during our wanking sessions, and most people also use fantasy during their sexual episodes with other people. Besides being tailor-made for our own needs and desires, the nice thing about fantasy is that it is completely private. You don't have to share it with anyone and so it can be as wild and shameful as you like, and you never have to explain!

We all havc our own personal favourites, but the sex researchers Masters and Johnson did a survey to find out what were the most common sexual fantasies enjoyed by gay men. This is the list in order of popularity:

1. Imagery of sexual anatomy – usually of penis or buttocks of someone other than their partner.
2. Forced sexual encounters. In nearly all instances the gay men fantasised themselves as the rapist.
3. Encounters with women - usually women from the gay man's past.
4. Having idyllic anonymous sex with an attractive stranger is a strong fantasy image. These day-dreams usually revolve around a work colleague, entertainer or some other person seen and fancied from a distance.
5. Group sex – the fantasiser often imagines himself observing an orgy rather than participating in it.

It is sometimes possible to share fantasies with our partner to good effect, and even to act them out. Playing out "scenes" has always been a popular pastime for the S&M crowd, and now it is being taken up by a wider audience: many gay men are experimenting with "acting out".

Think of a scenario which excites you and then play it out as though you were starring in a porn video. Remember, you've got to satisfy the jaded appetites of your audience, so you will need to be particularly imaginative and inventive in the things you do, and where you do them. You don't have to be Sir Ian McKellen to play a part. So if you are acting the school master who likes to spank his pupils, adopt an appropriate tone of voice and say the right things. This will occasionally result in fits of nervous giggles that can spoil the atmosphere. After all, really good sex fantasies are not funny! You need imagination to take your partner's temporary persona seriously, particularly if he is a bad actor. This will only work if you are both prepared to really fantasise that you are two different people. Once you've assumed the identity of these other characters (who are, of course, incredibly depraved and filthy in their sexual desires) you can permit yourself to do absolutely anything you want.

Let's start with that old favourite, The Delivery Boy sketch. Here's the script. You are under the shower, innocently soaping your groin, when the door bell rings. You can only find a skimpy towel to wrap around yourself, leaving acres of flesh exposed. You open the door and there is the humpy pizza delivery boy (cast in order of appearance: you, your lover). You invite the delivery boy in while you find the money to pay for the foodstuff, and discover that this is his last delivery for the night, and he is available for other activities. Your towel "accidentally" falls off, inflaming the randy delivery boy.

As you are now "in character", you can make demands on each other that you wouldn't ordinarily do. ("You've let my pizza get cold! Get over the back of that settee, I'm going to smack your arse till it shines!" "You like that big dick, dontcha?" etc. etc.)

If you've sometimes fantasised about a big, blonde bobby handcuffing you before giving you a "bang" with his truncheon then pop down to the fancy dress hire shop and see what you can arrange. (This is one for the privacy of your own home, though. It is illegal for anyone other than a policeman to wear a police uniform, or anything approximating one, in the street.) Ex-army clothing shops, theatrical suppliers and jumble sales are happy hunting grounds for fantasy clothes and items of apparel that can be converted into objects of desire.

If your fantasy demands a location that is not, strictly speaking, private, such as a beach or wood or back alley, then be very careful about it. There are few places these days that are people-free for very long.

And again, if your fantasy involves harm or violence to, or coercion of, other people, then it might be better to leave that one safely inside your head, unless your partner is willing to simulate some of the things that you want.

FEET

Feet are quite often the object of fetish and many people get turned on by them. Some men like to lick and suck their partner's toes, to lick the bottom of their feet and generally play around with those strangely desirable attachments at the bottom of our legs. Feet are fun!

Try this: instead of finger-fucking what about toe-fucking? A foot fetishist of my acquaintance tells me that he is in heaven when his boyfriend sticks his toes up my friend's arse and wiggles them. Closely cropped toenails for this one, please.

To the foot faddist all things to do with the feet are sexy: socks, shoes, corn plasters, the lot! Some like clean feet, some like them smelly, some like black business socks and some like the white, athletic type. Feet clad in Doc Marten's are beauty incarnate to some eyes. In olden times shoes had long, pointy toes, which were supposed to be phallic in suggestion. When sitting at the table, opposite a lover, men would stretch out their leg, put their pointy shoe up their ladies dress and frig her with it.

Like all fetishes, those obsessed with feet can become a bit of a bore when they neglect other parts of the body, but generally their passion *a pieds* can be a turn-on.

FELCHING

or velch or fletch, describes the practice of ejaculating into someone's anus and then sucking the semen out again. This is so obviously dangerous that it cannot be recommended as a practice – however alluring it may seem to some people.

FETISH

Fetish is from the Latin word meaning 'artificial'. It was originally an object which was worshipped, but then was taken over by psychologists to explain a phenomenon whereby people become sexually aroused by the thought or presence of inanimate objects and substances or particular parts of the body.

Fetishism is very widespread in the gay world, witness the popularity of leather, denim, rubber-ware and other clothing which stimulates sexual feelings. Because of their association with sexual situations with desirable men and the promise of excitement, these materials have become eroticised in the minds of many people.

Most exotic fetishes usually start in early childhood. One case history I read concerned a man who had a fetish about car exhaust pipes. Apparently, as a small child he had been riding in the back seat of his parents car, kneeling up to look out through the rear window. There he watched the fumes coming from the exhaust pipe. At the same time, the motion of the car was rubbing his penis against the seat of the car, and eventually caused him to have his first – and very intense – orgasm. After that he found that he could not have sex unless he either fantasised about exhaust pipes or actually had one in his presence. He even had to have one in bed with him when he made love to his wife! This is perfectly true – proving not only that truth is stranger than fiction, but that fetishes can be a real pain. If the fetish object *must* be present whenever you are engaged in sex, then the focus narrows in a way that becomes very boring for partners who don't feel the same way about it.

Of course, fetishes don't have to be objects, they can be smells (one man couldn't perform unless he had a particular perfume in the room) or places (the back of a car, on the stairs, on the draining board etc. etc.).

Psychologists have labelled fetishes "abnormal" but if they only amount, for instance, to a lust for corduroy or jock-straps to be incorporated into sexual activity, they don't strike me as being harmful.

Fingering

Sometimes called 'frigging'. There are other slang terms for this activity, like 'diddling' and 'stink-finger'.

The fingers are excellent sex toys and can be put to a hundred and one different uses. Perhaps the most popular is fingering and penetrating the anus. This is an excellent pre-cursor to intercourse, as it loosens up the sphincter, but it can be pleasurable in its own right, too. Use a bit of lubricant, make sure the nails are cut down and there are no jagged edges, and ensure that you aren't wearing any rings with sharp corners. Gently massage the arsehole for a while (an extremely pleasant sensation for the recipient. Why not try it mutually?). Insert the finger, if penetration is desired, and shag away with it. Some people like the number of digits to be increased after a while. Be gentle and, as in fucking, let the person who is being fingered dictate the rate of penetration and the violence of thrusting.

From a safer sex point of view there is a small risk involved in this activity. It can be overcome with condoms over the fingers or a pair of rubber surgical gloves.

Fisting

Fist-fucking ('anobrachial intercourse' or 'handballing') is a specialist activity that is only for the well-experienced and the foolhardy. Inserting the whole fist, and forearm into someone's anus is a dangerous pastime for the person on the receiving end. It is so easy for the lining of the anus to be damaged by such gross intrusion, and for infections to start up. Peritonitis, a dangerous inflammation, may ensue, and can prove fatal.

Practitioners of fist-fucking sometimes use calving gloves, those long-sleeved rubber items which farmers use for delving into the innards of cows.

If you have been fist fucked and you feel any kind of abdominal pain afterwards, get medical attention immediately. According to research by Project Sigma at the South Bank University, 17 per cent of their study sample of gay men had fisted at some point in their sex life, although only 1 per cent had done it in the past month. This perhaps indicates that it's not an experience many people care to repeat.

The practise of fisting came to public attention in 1993, when the term was used on national television by the gay comedian Julian Clary causing much sensation and chattering in Britain's ridiculous tabloid press.

FOLLY BELLS

In the seventeenth century, young dudes would attach little bells to their codpieces to attract attention to that department and to indicate that sex was available on request. Is this a custom which ought to be revived? It would save an awful lot of shilly-shallying.

FOOD

Is food sexy? The question must be asked because man has, for centuries, been searching for those aphrodisiac substances that would aid lovemaking and make him more libidinous. Over the years many foods have been credited with aphrodisiac properties, usually expensive or hard-to-find things like asparagus, champagne, truffles and caviar. These are the foods we are most likely to eat on special occasions, such as intimate dinners shared with someone whom we hope later to shag. Maybe this is why such things have this reputation. Other foods which have, at some time or another, been rumoured to promote sexual desire are: chocolate, mussels, Guinness, rhubarb, apricots, claret and passion fruit. The supposed aphrodisiac qualities of oysters were spoiled for me, though, when I heard Lily Savage describe them as "snot on an ashtray".

Casanova favoured Parma ham because he said its tender pinkness "felt like another tongue in my mouth". Pepita Aris, writing about aphrodisiacs said that "Rawness and mouth-feel seen to be linked. Raw salmon and gravadlax, like Parma ham, carry a suggestion of intimate flesh."

Asparagus, because of its suggestive phallic shape, has always been popular as a food of love. However, it can give urine a terrible smell very soon after it has been eaten, and therefore anyone contemplating golden showers (q.v.) as part of their love play should avoid it.

Food need not, of course, always be eaten off a plate. Much fun and entertainment can be had from using your partner's cock as a serving platter. Are you fond of whipped cream? Spread it on your boyfriend's member and gently suck it off again. It will have become imbued with a delicate but attractive flavour. Or what about a peanut butter snack, or jam or, for the figure-conscious, plain, low-fat yoghurt?

One man I know swears by Chedaree. He says it almost smells like the real thing. Now ensure that you lick up every last morsel! One of those spray cans of strawberry mousse allows the food item to be easily placed almost anywhere for licking off. Spray it between the legs, on the belly, on the lips – anywhere you will enjoy slurping it up again.

Of course food is not only good for stimulating the sense of taste, it can also provide stimulation in other areas. The carrot, courgette, cucumber and banana have all been employed to good effect. After all, why should nuns have all the fun in their convent garden? Buttered corn on the cob has never been better employed than when it makes its warm entrance into a receptive anus. Try not to use fruit or veg. that is too ripe as this tends to break during the festivities.

Considering the use of food and drink as a means of seduction, Ogden Nash wrote: 'Candy is a dandy, but liquor is quicker'.

FOUR LIPS

This is a variation for three participants (see Three-way). One stands, while the other two kneel at either side of him, facing each other. The two in the kneeling position then kiss, with the standing man's penis between their four lips. He can then thrust, or they can move their heads up and down his shaft in unison. In effect he is having a double blow-job. This is high up on the list of safer sex tricks as no penetration occurs.

FROTTAGE

Strictly speaking this means rubbing yourself against someone for sexual stimulation while clothed. Thus, London commuters sometimes get men rubbing up against them in the rush hour tube. An old joke about this goes:

"What's that in your trousers that's sticking into me?"

"Oh, it's just my wage packet."

"Then you must have had a rise!"

Frottage is now used to describe any kind of rubbing together for sexual purposes. It has taken on a new popularity in these days of safer sex. You can lay on top of each other, belly-to-belly, and thrust away for as long as you like. Naturally, the penis can be rubbed against just about any part of a partner's body. Use a bit of lubrication to make it more comfortable. Then put your mind to work to think what other parts of your body would feel good if they were rubbed together.

FUCKING

Fucking, shagging, humping, bumming, buggery, sodomy, anal intercourse – the list of terms for this particular activity seem endless (see under Euphemisms for more). For gay men, it usually means pushing the penis into the partner's anus and thrusting. It's the sexual act that the popular mind most associates with homosexuals, and the one heterosexuals have the most problem with. Or so they say. In actual fact, straights indulge in anal sex far more frequently than they care to admit. Sometimes they do it because there is no effective contraception available and sometimes just because they like it. One survey said that as many as 30 per cent of straights had used anal intercourse as part of their love-making at some time. The strange anomaly is that anal intercourse is still illegal for heterosexuals, but has been decriminalised for homosexuals over the age of 18 in private. At last! A piece of discrimination that favours us.

So, how popular is anal intercourse with homosexuals? Well, according to research, not very. Project Sigma found that "anal intercourse is not a particularly frequent part of the sexual repertoire, even among men who currently engage in the activity." They said that it is far from being the universal gay practice that the straight world likes to think, and "a significant proportion of gay men have never engaged in it at all."

How important, then, is fucking to gay men? According to the Sigma's research findings, 92 per cent of the gay men they interviewed said that they had fucked or been fucked at some time in their sex life. In the previous month, 41 per cent said they had engaged in fucking – either as the active or passive partner or in both roles. The average mean age when people had their first fuck was 20.9 years.

Sodomy brings out a particularly strong revulsion in some heterosexuals. This may be because they think any activity which centres round the anus must be dirty, or it may be that they are discomfited by the whole idea of a man being penetrated – a role which they maintain is 'naturally' female. In some Latin countries there is a special contempt reserved for men who allow themselves to be penetrated, a contempt which does not apply to those who take the active role. In Nicaragua the dismissive term for the passive partner in anal intercourse is *cochon,* while in Mexico and Brazil it is *bicha.*

Many gay men now consider much less than they did that they haven't had "real" sex unless fucking was involved. Because anal intercourse is undoubtedly the single most common means of acquiring and passing HIV for gay men, its desirability as the central focus of sex has to be questioned. There is nothing moralistic about this – I'm well aware of the strong appeal fucking has for some gay men – but if we want to check the spread of HIV and Aids, we really must look honestly at this question.

Most people who've taken the trouble to find out about HIV will be aware that it passes more easily through homosexual intercourse because the lining of the anal canal is so much more delicate than that of the vagina. During a vigorous anal fuck, the lining of the anus can become damaged, and this can then allow infected semen to get straight into the blood stream. One barrier against this is, of course, condoms and, although they are better than nothing, they are far from 100 per cent certain protection. They can break, come off, leak. A survey by Which? magazine tested 17,000 condoms and found that 9 of the 34 brands failed, including three which carry the kitemark – hitherto considered a guarantee of quality. There are several brands that are advertised as 'super strong' and have been specially made for anal intercourse. Experiments are taking place to find another, stronger substance from which to make condoms.

If you're determined to have anal sex, remember before you start: always use a lubricant (a water-based one such as KY will not damage the condom in the way that oil-based ones such as Vaseline, olive oil, butter etc. will). Adequate lubrication will make the fuck much more pleasurable for the person on the receiving end. Trying to fuck someone 'dry' can be very painful indeed, even if you manage to get the dick in in the first place. Try to avoid getting lubricant inside the condom, as this makes it much more likely to slip off. Of course, in the movies you will see people apparently managing with saliva; this is not enough in ordinary circumstances.

For the man being fucked, it can be a painful experience if he has not mastered the art of relaxing the anal sphincter (the tight muscle surrounding the opening of the arsehole). To be blunt, the job of the sphincter is to keep shit in until it's convenient for you to evacuate, at which time you relax the muscle and let it out. You've been doing this ever since you were a kid, so you know that you have some control over the sphincter. But letting something move the other way (i.e. going in rather than out) is a different experience, and you have to learn all over again how to relax your sphincter and allow the rampaging member to ravage you. This, of course, is why being fucked can be a painful experience, and why it can be useful to spend some time trying to relax the sphincter and prepare it for the dick by gently massaging it with the fingers. But the most effective way of relaxing your arse is through your mind. You actually have to *persuade* it to relax.

It can take practice to master this skill, and some gay men give up anal sex because it was such a trauma the first few times they tried it.

For the man doing the fucking, remember to be gentle with your partner, and to listen to his instructions when trying to make the initial entry. It is no use simply trying to achieve the penetration by the breaking and entering method. If you push too hard initially it is likely that your partner will experience a searing pain which will be so intense he'll be seeing stars.

If he says "slowly" or "gently" or "push", then listen to him and co-operate. You are much more likely to have a satisfying fuck if you take your time making the entry than if you go charging in there like a bull in a china shop and, in the process, hurting your partner.

Buggery (makes it sound particularly filthy and forbidden if we call it that, doesn't it?) lends itself to many positions. Most popular with gay men are "doggy-fashion" (on hands and knees); and "missionary" (with the fuckee on his back with his legs in the air, and the fucker on top, sometimes with his partners legs over his shoulders). A small pillow under the small of the back can facilitate this position and make it easier if you're doing it in bed, or if there is a significant difference in your heights. Similarly if you are doing it on a table (very convenient, I have to say), a shorter person might need something to stand on in order to be able to comfortably bring arse and cock into contact. The other most frequently used position is with one man laying flat on his tummy with the partner on top.

Then there is the squatting position, where the insertor lays on his back while his partner squats over him and gradually sits on the penis. He is then free to bounce up and down to his heart's content, bringing joy and gladness to all those present. It also gives the person who is being penetrated a degree of control which he doesn't have in other positions. When he gets tired, his prone partner can begin thrusting by arching his back and pushing his buttocks up and down. The top man in this instance can position himself facing toward his partner or facing away. The advantages are that in facing forward he can kiss and fondle his partner's tits, while in facing away, his partner gets to see the penetration in all its glory.

Sitting in a chair is another possibility. Once again, the penetrated partner sits on the penis of his friend who is comfortably ensconced in his favourite chair. Got a rocking chair? Aren't you lucky! Again, the choice is to face each other or do it back to front. In the former circumstances, the partner who is bouncing up and down on the cock also gets to have his own organ stimulated on the chest of his lover. Facing away, the lover can reach round and play with the bouncer's cock.

Stepladders also hold possibilities for those who are imaginative and adventurous enough to exploit them, as do coffee tables (which hopefully have been checked beforehand to ensure that they are strong enough to support the sometimes hefty demands of rumpy-pumpy). One person squats on the edge of the table, allowing his lover to approach his widely spread cheeks from behind.

Bending over a kitchen work surface and putting one leg up onto it can also cause the cheeks of the arse to spread in a most gratifying fashion.

Once again, the only way to explore anal intercourse with a semi-clear conscience is by using condoms, unless you are absolutely certain about the health status of yourself and your partner (and who can be these days – other than, perhaps, Garry Bushell, and who'd want to fuck him anyway?). Even those who are both HIV positive should still use condoms. There is more than one strain of the virus and it is important not to acquire any other bugs which might trigger HIV infection into becoming full blown Aids.

Once you have made the entry, and you are thrusting happily away, you may want to vary things a little by rotating your hips or pushing the penis in at different angles. Be careful with all this because, as we've said, the inside of the anus is very delicate and fragile and won't take kindly to being bashed and thrashed by an over-enthusiastic dick. The person who has been screwed may feel sore for a day or two after a particularly hefty session, but often it is simply a warm feeling of having had a hard massage.

One man I spoke to said that he always found anal intercourse extremely painful and unpleasant, but felt he was letting his partner down if he didn't do it. As he grew older and more confident, he came to the conclusion that no, he didn't *have* to have anal sex if he didn't want to. It was his body after all. He says: "I felt liberated when I realised that I didn't have to get fucked any more. I started to enjoy sex when I knew it wasn't going to end in this excruciatingly painful activity."

The message is – don't do it if you don't want to.

Read about safer sex, find out about condoms and if you really can't resist fucking, then make sure you use one every time.

Glans

This is the conical bit on the end of the penis. Its underside is where many of the nerves that provide the pleasure are situated, so always give it plenty of attention in sex play. In the uncircumcised, the glans can be a little bit tender when it comes out to play, so be careful with teeth or sharp finger-nails.

Glory holes

Glory holes are those apertures drilled in the walls that separate stalls in public lavatories. Habitués live in hope that someone will poke interesting things through from the other side.

If the boys in blue arrive, thee is less chance of their being able to get you for anything if you are in separate loo-stalls. If there is a raid you simply stuff up the connecting orifice, and then plead that you are horrified by the dirty-minded suggestions of ploddish persons: it never occurred to you that people got up to such disgraceful things.

These days, with the hi-tech use of video surveillance and fibre-optic technology, the odds are stacked against you. The police seem capable of putting almost limitless resources into convicting piss-palace partygoers. You'd think they'd have more to do with their time, what with all the crime and mugging on the streets. (Yours faithfully, disgusted, Earls Court).

The drawback to glory holes is that you have to put an awful lot of trust in the boy next door. Sticking your precious pecker through the hole and leaving it to the mercy of someone unknown can be quite a hair-raising prospect. I have had nightmares about such scenarios. Suppose, for instance, that the next stall-holder is not as friendly as you thought and has a Stanley Knife.

Ugh!

Golden shower

Urolagnia, lindinism or pissing on each other. Water Sports (q.v.), as aficionados know it, has a large body of devotees. There seems little harm in this pastime as urine is sterile when it emerges from the body and, indeed, there are those people who swear by drinking their own urine as a health regime. The actress Sarah Miles has come out as a piss-taker, and drinks a glass of her own wee-wee every morning, claiming that it replaces many of the essential salts that the body needs to function effectively. Urine is comprised of 95 per cent water into which are dissolved waste products such as urea, uric acid and mineral salts, as well as traces of metabolic by-products.

In former times it was used as a shampoo and in industrial processes. Nowadays the medical profession is becoming aware of the almost magical properties of urine in the search for new and effective drugs for a whole range of afflictions.

Project Sigma rated golden showers as an "uncommon" sexual activity among British gay men. They found that 28 per cent of their respondents had tried it at some point in their sex lives, but in the month before the survey only 3 per cent had done it. Obviously this is one that people like to experiment with, but most find they don't like it.

Those who do like to piss on each other for sexual kicks do it for different reasons. Humiliation – that most potent of sexual motives – is one. Not everyone agrees that watersports necessarily have to be sado-masochistic, though. Havelock Ellis in his *Studies in the Psychology of Sex* wrote: "The impulse to bestow a symbolic value on the act of urination in a beloved person is not extremely uncommon...when existing in only a slight degree, it must be regarded as within the normal limits of variation of sexual emotion."

Most Golden Showers are enjoyed in the bath, by far the most convenient place. Covering the bed with a waterproof tarpaulin is favoured by some, but inevitably there is more piss than anticipated and it starts running on the floor. Urine's strong aroma soon permeates rugs and carpets and gets stronger as the days pass. Although urine is sterile when it first emerges from the body, it rapidly absorbs bacteria from the environment and begins to smell. If you persist in pissing in your bedroom, it is soon likely to smell like a geriatric ward at the local hospital. (It also tastes and smells particularly unpleasant after the pisser has eaten asparagus.)

The Surgeon General of the United States has said that urine is not a mode of transmission for HIV, so if you want to piss into your partner's mouth – which some people do – then there seems little medical reason to restrain you.

Gonorrhoea

Gonorrhoea – often referred to as "the clap" or "a dose" – is one of the commonest of the sexually transmitted diseases and is rampant among active gay men. Fortunately it can be treated very quickly and successfully with penicillin or some other antibiotic. So, if you suspect you might have picked up a dose, then pop along to your nearest Special Clinic (or Department of Genito-Urinary Medicine, or whatever name they're using in your area) and have it checked out.

Gonorrhoea is transmitted by close bodily contact and, in men, is usually found in the urethra (the tube down which pee and semen come). It isn't just a disease of the genitals, though, and it can enter through any of the mucous membranes so you might get infected through your rectum, throat, mouth or eyes.

Perhaps the first indication you will have of a gonorrhoeal infection is a thick discharge of pus from the penis. You might notice it in your pyjamas or underpants. There might be a burning sensation when you take a leak. If you've got it in the throat, you might have symptoms that feel something like a common cold. If it's in your eyes there will be tears, irritation and pus. If you've been infected anally there might be soreness accompanied by a constant urge to defecate. Bowel movements might be preceded by a spurt of yellow pus.

Sometimes, however, the disease is sneaky and you don't have any noticeable symptoms at all. If this is the case, and the infection is left untreated, you might develop a form of arthritis which particularly affects the knees, ankles, elbows and wrists. If you get it in the eyes, you could become blind.

Have regular check ups at the special clinic and to use condoms at all times.

GRAFFITI

Messages or drawings that are written, painted or scratched on to walls. Graffiti is still common in public lavatories when potential cottagers leave little messages for each other advising when they will next be soliciting for immoral purposes. "Thursday, 3pm for sex fun. Big cock" was the alluring graffito which I read each week as a child when visiting the bog at my local swimming pool. It was etched with great determination into the wood, so I assumed whoever had done it was serious in his offer. But, however many Thursday afternoons I spent hanging around that loo, Mr Big Cock never arrived and the sex fun was always restricted to wandering in and out of the showers, checking out the talent there.

I wonder if those hopeful messages ever result in successful trysts?

And, of course, graffiti gives great scope for wits to amuse an audience it will never meet. Perhaps the best known scrawled message read: "My mother made me a homosexual." With the response "If I gave her the wool, would she make me one?"

Over a urinal once I saw the inscription "More than three shakes constitutes a wank." And another famous one reads: "Horny, ten inches of man muscle. Will do anything. Ring Randy on 1234. P.S. If you read this, Kevin, it's only me, Brian."

The writer Kenneth Ingram claimed that before the First World War, graffiti on lavatory walls was almost always heterosexual in nature, but after 1930 it was "almost invariably homosexual."

GREEK LOVE

This is yet another euphemism for gay sex. Right from Victorian times homosexuality was referred to as "Greek love" because classical scholars would have us believe that homosexuality was institutionalised in ancient Greece. It's true that the male form was worshipped and admired in the cradle of civilisation – you just have to look at some of the paintings and sculpture from that period for confirmation. Plato wrote of this phenomenon in *Charmides:*

"What do you think of the young man, Socrates?" asked Khairephon. "Doesn't he have a handsome face?"

"Marvellously so!" I said.

"Well," he said "if he'll only take his cloak off, you'll forget he has a face at all, he's so overwhelmingly beautiful to look at."

But that doesn't mean to say that homosexuality was tolerated in the way that we'd like to imagine. It was as much to do with excluding women from a full role in society as anything else.

After all, if you go into W.H. Smith and look on the magazine shelf marked "Sport", you will see picture after picture of over-developed and under-dressed men. The muscle mags are surely the modern-day equivalent of the Discus Thrower of old. And most of these magazines are bought by other straight men, proving that the muscular male form is still idolised – even though there is no discernible tolerance of homosexuality from the men who like to buy "Muscle Illustrated."

No, ancient Greece was only slightly more tolerant of gay love than modern Britain is. There were no gay couples living in societally approved bliss in the Athens of old.

What *was* institutionalised was *paedia,* when a younger men would be taken under the wing of an older man who would act as his teacher and mentor. In return the young men were required to let their charges fuck them. The society of the day demanded that both parties to this arrangement eventually be married and live conventionally in all other respects. There was nothing "gay" about these relationships. The writers Warren J. Blumenfeld and Diane Raymond put it this way in their book *Looking at Gay and Lesbian Life:* "Though it was common for a boy to engage in sexual relations with his teacher and even for soldiers to be lovers, one should not assume that ancient Greek society gave wholehearted approval to all expressions of same-sex attraction. After the age of nineteen or so, the young man was expected to marry and establish a family. Those who did not, or who continued to engage in homosexual relationships exclusively were subject to ridicule or worse. In addition, exclusive sexual passivity in men met with criticism and at times treated severely."

We are led to believe that homosexuality was encouraged among the Greek army, so that the men would fight more fiercely in order to protect their lovers who would be beside them on the battlefield. This fairy tale has always rung hollow to my ears. Judging by the number of dishonourable discharges each year from modern British Forces there is still an army of lovers, but very little gaiety.

Grope

Your hand reaches down to his crotch area and begins to close over the object of desire. You squeeze gently, and there is evidence of a swelling in the pants. You are ***groping*** your sexual contact. This is probably the very first overt move towards the genitals that you've made. Groping is really a statement of intent. You've had a bit of a snog and now you want to go further. A gentle grope will give your companion the message and allow him to either reply in kind or firmly lead your hand away from the area, the signal that it ain't going to happen – at least without a further bit of persuasion.

Groping is a useful skill to have, and worth a bit of practice. Try to discover on which side your intended partner "dresses" (as they say in the tailoring trade). Be careful how you grasp when you're down there, the wearing of tight trousers might already be constricting the balls, and further pressure can be uncomfortable. So take it gently. Then rub or squeeze. After a while you can unzip the pants and insert the hand inside, continuing to grope as you go. If you're standing while snogging (perhaps on the dance floor), you might be able to get your hand into his pants at the back and fondle and finger his arse. This is one advantage of not wearing a belt – access into the pants is much easier without!

As the phrase "groping in the dark" indicates, most groping is done blind. You are probably engaged facially already, deep throat kissing, and the wandering hands have to find their own way to the target. Somehow they manage it – and without the aid of a guide dog.

Gross indecency

This is the insulting legal term which is applied to gay sex when it comes up before the courts. The only "gross" aspect of it must surely refer to the dirty minds of the men whose duty it is to enforce our crazy sex laws. Moralising magistrates are very fond of giving lectures to those men unlucky enough to come up before them after being apprehended in a cottage or on the Heath. But have they forgotten the biblical adage "Judge not lest ye be judged"? I think the policemen and the JPs who seem to delight in "processing" cottagers must have a screw loose. What other explanation could there be for the evident pleasure they get in either fitting people up (via the pretty police) or fining them large amounts. In this list of Establishment sickos, I also include the editors of local newspapers who like to compliment themselves on their own moral superiority by printing the full names and addresses of people who have already been humiliated in the Magistrates Court on a charge of gross indecency. Must ensure the neighbours know!

If you like to meet your partners in places which are regarded as "public", ensure that you know your rights under the law. If you think the police have overstepped their powers, get a solicitor and fight them in the Crown Court in front of a jury. Unfortunately charges are increasingly being made under local bye-laws which means no jury or legal aid – and your very own entry in the Police National Computer.

If you do get the chance to have your case heard at a Crown Court, statistics show that you are more likely to get off if you defend yourself.

And anyway, "gross indecency" sounds like fun to me.

Group sex

In Roman times group sex was an organised institution. The orgy (q.v.) was originally a secret ritual used to pay homage to various gods, especially Bacchus. Nowadays orgies are still held in secret, but that's because the gay variety at least is illegal. Which is not to say that they don't happen, and that one day you might be invited to one.

Orgies aren't everyone's goblet of vino, and the prospect of having a room full of people finding out your little secrets – like a spotty back or droopy bum – might be a bit off-putting to some. But if you aren't the shy and retiring sort, you might enjoy it. A friend of mine who likes this kind of thing says that he will only participate if everyone else in the room is a stranger. He finds it difficult to watch his friends having sex and then take them seriously the following day. He says that he has tried group sex in bath houses, saunas and the back rooms of various bars in New York, and he found it most exhilarating, because it was mainly in the dark and no-one spoke. Only groaning is allowed so, while hands wander and dirty demands come out of the blackness, fantasy can be given full reign. He says that when people start talking to him in such situations – even if it's dirty talk to enhance pleasure – he loses interest instantly. This, for him, has to be the kind of totally self-gratifying sex – no conversation, little eye contact and a lot of body language.

Of course, most of us have attended orgies vicariously, through the medium of sex videos, but these carefully choreographed Bacchanals appear to be the domain of only the fittest, handsomest young dudes. In these fantasies no-one ever fumbles with the KY tube, no-one ever fails to get an erection, no-one is ever ticklish, and nobody is overweight or utterly repulsive. The suburban orgy, however – the one that you and I are most likely to attend – will have its share of older, less perfectly sculpted specimens. When the order of the day is "no refusals", you might find yourself having to submit to the demands of people you can't stand the sight of.

Group sex requires a bit of imagination if full advantage is to be taken of the situation. What's the point of having access to all those cocks at one time without making something of it? The prospect of having every orifice filled at one time is very appealing, but I think the sensory overload, and the multiple necessity to simultaneously please all these demanding men, might make it difficult for the recipient to enjoy the experience very much. Still, I think most of us would be prepared to give it a go.

G-STRING

Sometimes called posing pouches, these are those small triangular pieces of white material which are affixed to the crotch area by bits of string passing round the waist, between the legs and cheeks of the arse. Their invention is attributed to the American Indian, and it was from this original design that the G-string was adapted, with the addition of spangles and tassels, to suit the chorus girls of old.

After vaudeville had finished with it, the posing pouch became very popular in the fifties and sixties in male "physique magazines". When the depiction of total male nudity was not permissible in magazines, G-strings provided the absolute minimum cover in order to allow eroticism without arrest. Perhaps the great populariser of the posing pouch in the gay community was the Athletic Model Guild of Los Angeles, a venerable institution founded in 1945.

During the sixties (which were far from swinging for most gay men), this organisation produced a pocket magazine called *Physique Pictorial* – ostensibly a body-building journal, which carried grainy, but highly erotic photographs of men in various stages of physical display. No full frontals were permitted at first, so the outstanding features of many models were adorned by posing pouches. Many of these were so heavily filled and bulging that one wondered how on earth they didn't just burst. For many of us, such titillation was far more exciting than having the whole works on display. The wet G-string has an appeal all its own. Bob Meizer, founder of AMG, tells that because he was taking photographs of strapping young men for decades, he actually had prospective models looking through his portfolio and finding photographs of their own fathers which he had taken twenty-five years previously.

Moving into the seventies, and attitudes relaxed a little. *Physique Pictorial* became more and more suggestive. Increasing numbers of its photos featured more than one model. At first these duos consisted of fairly mild "wrestling" poses, with bulging G-strings tantalisingly thrust forward. Then, pushing the boundaries a little further with each issue, and fighting court case after court case, the situations in which the models were featured became blatant, with whips, leather boots, spread cheeks etc. They would be shown in intimate situations – washing each down in the shower, helping each other with "press-ups" and so on. By the end of the seventies, the G-strings had been abandoned and not only was full nudity the norm, but erections and reasonably blatantly sexual poses were featured.

Bob Meizer is now recognised as an artist and an innovator. He has even been honoured by having his work featured in a coffee table book from the Gay Men's Press. His photographs provided the material for a million wank fantasies, and the G-string is still a favoured garment for many strippers and models – as is the sailor's hat which adorned just about every one of his muscle-men. It's good to see that some of the Athletic Model Guild's erotic films are now available on video – given that they were obliged to be so indirect, it's amazing that their titilatory qualities were so arousing.

The bane of many gay men's lives, guilt is that awful feeling that starts somewhere in the pit of the stomach and ends up in the head – in the form of depression. From the day we are born people are telling us that it's not good to be gay. Sometimes they tell us outright, sometimes they do it in more subtle ways. But we all pick up the message. It takes years and years to overcome that strange gut-feeling that what we are doing, what we are feeling, is wrong.

But we have to keep working at it. Guilt keeps so many gay men from getting what they really want out of life. Some deny themselves sex completely because they've fallen for the argument that two men shouldn't love each other. Some gay men can't make relationships with members of their own sex because they are eaten up with fear that one day the relationship will be exposed.

Never mind what other people say – whether those other people are your parents, your church, your doctor or whoever – you are entitled to express yourself in the way that is right for you. Some church leaders try to guilt-trip us into celibacy, forgetting that they are asking of us something which most of them aren't prepared to give themselves. The meanness, selfishness and cruelty of such demands should be resisted. We are all entitled to a sex life, and although celibacy is an option that is exercised by some, it is one that should be undertaken with a free conscience, not one that is imposed from above by some smug individual who isn't prepared to practise what he preaches.

Guilt has its place, of course, and most people would agree that it is necessary for us to sometimes feel guilty in order to make life tolerable – for instance, if we harm other people. Only a psychopath is totally free of guilt and remorse, and not many of us would want to be lumped together with the Yorkshire Ripper or Denis Nilsen. But loving other people is not a reason to feel guilty, it's a reason to celebrate.

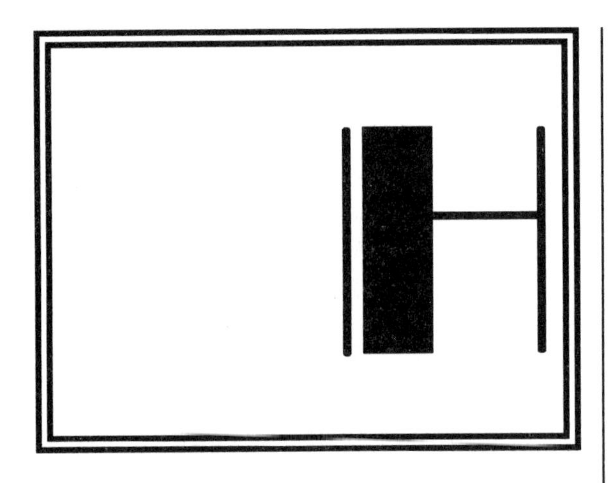

Body hair has different meanings for different people. There are those who are turned on by a hirsute chest, and those who find it utterly repellent. In these days of working out and body culture, it is fashionable to keep the chest hairless in order to fully display the fruits of one's labours at the gym. It's no use spending hour after hour (and a small fortune) developing prominent pecs, only to have their contours masked by a mat of bushy, black hair. Therefore, out comes the depilatory cream, the wax, the razors and whatever other means can be employed to keep the body free of hair.

And so, the most fabulous male physiques which are currently on display are invariably hairless. Have you ever seen a Chippendale with curlers on his chest? Do you see strippers with oil dripping off their chest rug? Goodness knows what agonies they go through in order to keep the grass from growing.

But recently my eye was caught by a model on the front of a copy of *Playgirl*. He was a hairy article – complete with facial stubble, hairy chest and hirsute abdomen. He seemed so out of place among the other bald bodies, and yet he had a kind of sexy threat about him. Here was an unreconstructed brute of a man who didn't apologise for having an exclusively male characteristic. There are plenty of us out here who love to bury ourselves in a prickly, thick jungle of hair. A man with hair on his chest has traditionally been seen as "potent" and "virile" and maybe slightly beastly – the King Kong legend lives on.

So why, in the public representation of the male form, are we being presented with a relentless diet of the glabrous? A few gorilla-esque hunks from time to time would be very welcome.

Hair on the head is a different matter. We've already covered baldness, but for those who have plenty of hair on their head there are endless opportunities for shaping and changing It's amazing what a difference a carefully-chosen hairstyle can make to a face. I see a huge range of imaginative cuts and shapes out among the gay community, many of them extremely attractive. Hairdressing may be seen in a stereotypical way as a "gay" profession, but when you consider the difference hair dressing has made on the way men look, it's obvious that the influence has been good. Just take a decko at photographs of men taken as recently as thirty years ago and you will see what I mean. The endless parade of short back and sides and Brylcreemed domes seems to indicate that everyone had hair like Curly Watts in those days. Even twenty-year olds looked middle-aged! Thank goodness for the gay sensibility in hairdressing: now we can all look good and we don't have to go to Vidal Sassoon to manage it.

Haemorrhoids

Piles, traditionally a subject of music hall jokes, aren't very funny for those who are afflicted. Haemorrhoids are basically varicose veins of the arse. They can occur inside the anus and outside, and they can be extremely painful. Naturally, if one is turned on by activities involving that particular region, piles can be extremely inconvenient. There is no truth in the rumour that anal sex can give you piles. However, someone did once say that for a sufferer from haemorrhoids, having anal sex was rather like giving birth to a set of broken crockery.

Straining on the loo can bring on piles, so to guard against getting them, eat a high fibre diet. There are creams that can reduce the swelling, but in severe cases surgery may be necessary.

Hepatitis B

Hepatitis B has been pushed into the background by the appearance of HIV, and yet it is a much more common infection among gay men, and potentially life-threatening. Hepatitis B is about 100 times more infectious than HIV, but it is spread in much the same kind of way, through bodily fluids. It's a blood-borne virus which attacks the liver. Past studies have shown as many as fifty per cent of gay men who were tested showed themselves to have antibody to the Hepatitis B virus, indicating infection at some time in the past.

Symptoms include tiredness, nausea, loss of appetite and aversion to drinking alcohol and to smoking. During the acute stage of the illness – that is, when it is most infectious – the sufferer's skin might become yellow, he will have a fever, dark urine, pale stools and abdominal tenderness in the area of the liver. Recovery takes up to six months, during which time the sufferer will be lethargic and depressed.

In about 50 per cent of cases there might be no symptoms at all, or they might be so mild that they aren't noticed. Most times the body fights off the virus and recovers, but in about ten per cent of cases a high level of the virus is retained and the individual becomes a carrier, even though he seems healthy.

There is no cure for hepatitis once it has been acquired, but the good news is that there is a very effective vaccine against it. You can get it on the National Health so, if you're an active gay man, rush to your GP and have the jabs. If he won't give them to you go along to the special clinic and ask them to do it for you. Alternatively you could pay to have it done privately, a small cost when compared to the consequences of a bout of hepatitis. That short course of injections could save you an awful lot of pain, inconvenience and wasted time.

Group to contact:

- Group B – for gay men who have or have had Hepatitis B – Tel: 0171-224 6514.

Herpes simplex can occur almost anywhere on the body, but because it can be spread by sexual contact, it is often found on the penis and anus. Those of us who have had herpes on our lips and mouth know what it feels like – it starts with an itch, develops into a painful blister, which eventually dries up, turns into a scab, drops off and we're back to normal. Until next time. Herpes, unfortunately, is for life. Once you've got the herpes virus, it lurks in your body, dormant most of the time, waiting until you're run down or depressed, and then resurfacing.

There are two strains of the same virus: Type I is associated with cold sores and Type II with genital lesions, although there may be some cross-over. By middle age, 95 per cent of the population are infected with Type I, although only 20 per cent show any symptoms. The Type II variety prefers the genitals and can be more persistent.

Genital herpes is particularly painful, and it is most important that you desist from sex when you have the blisters present on your body – they spread very easily. You aren't infectious, though, when the blisters and scabs have cleared up.

The first attack of herpes is often the worst and is often accompanied by flu-like symptoms with blisters appearing on the genitals or anus. After this, symptoms disappear and may never recur. Only one in ten sufferers are troubled by painful recurrence, according to the Herpes Association.

The only treatment at present is the drug acyclovir, which became available in 1981. It isn't a cure, it simply suppresses the symptoms. Some doctors think it should be kept for the chronic sufferers, others that it should be available to anyone who wants it. One leading expert on the condition thinks that anybody who gets herpes symptoms more than eight to 12 times a year should be on acyclovir permanently. It is quite an expensive drug to take on a daily basis and the long-term effects aren't known. Besides which, a recent American study has shown that acyclovir is beginning to lose its effectiveness for some people.

Some sufferers have found that relief from pain can be obtained by bathing in salt water.

Group to contact: Herpes Association, 41 North Road, Islington, London N7 9DP. Tel: 0171-607 9661.

Heterosexual and Homosexual

These words were coined by the Hungarian physician Karoly Martin Benkert in 1869. He created the word homosexual from the Greek *homo* – same and Latin *sexus* – sex. Since then the idea that there are two distinct and separate sexual orientations has caught on in a big way.

In the world of the tabloids – and in some gay people's minds – the human race is neatly divided into two components: those who like to have sex with the opposite gender (in *Sun*-speak, the "normal") and those who like to have sex with their own gender (which translates as "pervs" in tabloidese). These have been termed heterosexual and homosexual; gay and straight. Simple isn't it? Except it doesn't quite work like that.

The great sex researcher Alfred Kinsey suggested that in labelling ourselves homosexual (or gay or queer or whatever), we have created a rod for our own back. He suggested that there are no homosexuals or heterosexuals – only homosexual or heterosexual *sex acts*. We should not be using these terms as nouns but as adjectives. .

The idea of bisexuality is anathema to some people in the gay community, but Project Sigma has discovered in one of its surveys that as many as twenty-five per cent of men who think of themselves as gay also have sex with women.

Our sexual orientation is a measure of which gender we fancy most. It's all rather confused. I suppose in theory there are three orientations – heterosexual, homosexual and bisexual. But it isn't quite as simple as that. There is also situational sexuality – e.g. homosexual acts performed by heterosexual men who are in prisons or some other all-male institution where their preferred kind of sex is not available. These men are not 'homosexual', but they are behaving homosexually. Once out of prison, and back in the company of females, they wouldn't be interested in homosexual sex at all.

What then for those of us who are leading a whole lifestyle that reflects our predominant sexual desire, and not just occasionally indulging in sexual acts with members of our own sex? If I am not 'a homosexual', what am I?

It became necessary to invent a name for our sexuality, and that name is "gay". This self-applied label tells us – and whoever else we care to share it with – that we prefer to have sex *and emotional relationships* mainly or exclusively with other men. Or, as Christopher Isherwood put it: "It seems to me that the real clue to your sex-orientation lies in your romantic feelings rather than in your sexual feelings. If you are really gay, you are able to fall in love with a man, not just enjoy having sex with him."

So, gay people don't just perform "homosexual" acts, just as straight people don't just perform "heterosexual" acts – we each have a whole lifestyle which springs from our sexual orientation, be that gay or straight.

Which is not to say there is no overlap. You don't have to sign an affidavit when you label yourself "gay" or "straight" promising that you'll never have the other kind of sex. It applies as you want it to apply. Sexuality can be fluid and there is no question of a strict dividing line.

Bisexuals seem able to function well with both sexes – although there are degrees of preference. Kinsey expressed it as a scale from zero to six. Zero indicates that a person's preference is entirely heterosexual in nature, and he has never had a homosexual experience. Along the line – where most people are situated – there is a mixture of "largely homosexual, but with incidental heterosexual history" (5 on the scale); "largely homosexual, but with a distinct heterosexual history" (4 on the scale); "equally heterosexual and homosexual" (3); "largely heterosexual but with a distinct homosexual history" (2).

The other famous sex researchers, Masters and Johnson, did a major study of homosexuality back in the sixties, and during the course of this project, identified another group of people whose orientation did not fit any of the three already mentioned. This fourth orientation they named *ambisexual* and they defined it as "a man or woman who unreservedly enjoys, solicits or responds to overt sexual opportunity with equal ease and interest regardless of the sex of the partners, and who, as a sexually mature individual, has never evidenced any interest in a continuing relationship."

Ambisexuals differ from bisexuals in that they appear to have no preference – either sex will do in equal measure. But, you might say, wouldn't they qualify as 3s on the Kinsey scale? Apparently not. Those bisexuals who were interviewed by M&J and who had an equal history of heterosexual and homosexual relationships (3 on the scale), nearly always expressed a preference for one or the other – or were, at the time, living in a relationship which was either heterosexual in character or homosexual in character. Ambisexuals, on the other hand, were not interested in relationships of any description and could not express a preference for either men or women.

HIT PARADE

According to Project Sigma, these are the sexual acts which are most popular with gay men, followed by the percentage of men who have ever tried them. The high percentage for anal intercourse is heavily influenced by pre-AIDS activity:

- **Masturbation**
- Self: 99 and a half per cent.
- Someone else: 95 per cent.

- **Kissing**: 96 per cent

- **Fellatio**
- Been sucked: 96 per cent
- Sucked someone else: 95 per cent

- **Anal Fingering**: 90 per cent

- **Anal Intercourse**
- Been fucked: 85 per cent
- Fucked someone else: 85 per cent

- **Body Rubbing:** 84 per cent

- **Massage**: 81 per cent

- **Rimming**: 81 per cent

- **Inter-femoral intercourse**: 78 per cent

- **Corporal Punishment**: 41 per cent

- **Golden Showers**: 28 per cent (although only 3 per cent had done this in the month preceding the survey)

- **Fisting**: 17 per cent (1 per cent in the preceding month)

- **Douching:** 7 per cent (1 per cent in preceding month)

- **Scat**: 3 per cent (0 per cent in preceding month).

HOLIDAY SEX

Even old established couples will tell you that when they get on holiday their sexual interest in each other revives most pleasingly. I have been in a steady relationship with the same man for twelve years now, and although sex is still good, it is nowhere as frequent as it was at the beginning. This is a natural consequence of any relationship, however successful it might be. Get us away on holiday, though, and we suddenly become like rabbits. I don't know whether this is simply because there's more time for humpty-dumpty, whether it's because we're more relaxed and indulgent or simply because of the undoubted aphrodisiac quality of hotel rooms.

Those who are holidaying as singles are well catered for in the gay world. There are holiday companies that will whisk you off to resorts where sex is more or less on tap twenty-four hours a day. Contrary to the impression given by the brochures, you do not have to be a twenty-one year old hunk in order to enjoy the facilities at these resorts. Just about anyone can find a sexual partner if they check into a gay apartment complex or hotel.

There's sex, sun and invariably booze, and the combination can be heady. So heady, in fact, that you might be tempted to forget about safer sex. It's most important, if you're going on a holiday which will revolve around sex, to go well-prepared. Take plenty of condoms – extra strength and kite-marked – and, if you're having penetrative sex, use them.

Bon voyage!
(see also Tourism)

HOUSEHOLD EQUIPMENT

Lateral thinking is a useful skill to have when seeking new and inexpensive thrills in your sexual life. It may not be necessary to *buy* those expensive sex toys – just look around the house and see what alternative uses your existing appliances could be put to. That step-ladder in the garage, for instance, isn't just good for changing light bulbs or hanging wallpaper, you can have enormous fun experimenting with new positions on it. Ensure that it is stable though to remain upright when the action starts in earnest – after all, this is erotica, not Laurel and Hardy!

Similarly those who have never had sex on the stairs might be in for a pleasant surprise when they try it. Sliding down the banister can take on a whole new significance. The kitchen, too, has many possibilities; some of those little gadgets you bought, and subsequently shoved away in a drawer, might have more than one use; the food processor vibrates wonderfully and the fridge is probably packed with possibilities – some of which we have looked at already (in particular fresh cream and courgettes).

We have also explored the bathroom, and it has to be reiterated that this room is a veritable treasure trove of sensual experiences for those with a mind of sufficiently creative perversion to see them.

Next we visit the cleaning cupboard where those candles you keep for power cuts are stored. Remember the famous THT safer sex leaflet which heartily recommended the dripping of hot candle-wax onto flesh?

The sweeping brush has a very interesting handle with pleasantly rounded end, and those chamois leathers you've been cleaning the window with can feel very pleasant next to the skin.

Out in the garden shed, too, you might be able to extemporise. A friend of mine has broken the B&Q monopoly on D-I-Y by employing sandpaper in a most imaginative manner. And, of course, the shed itself may hold appeal as a forbidden location – almost outdoors, but private enough to shield you from the prying eyes of neighbours. Garden furniture might be stored there and if you've never had sex in a deckchair, you haven't lived.

In the bedroom, wire coat hangers have been used to interesting effect by more than just Joan Crawford. Bedside lamps can illuminate nooks, crannies and crevices which would, in normal circumstances, remain in shadow. There are often full-length mirrors around in dressing tables and wardrobes. And, indeed, having sex on top of the wardrobe is as time-honoured a variation as swinging from the chandeliers.

From bedroom to cellar (where many aficionados have installed their very own dungeon, with manacles, racks and other implements of torture and corporal punishment), there is, indeed, no place like home!

Housemaid's Knee

Housemaid's knee is a swelling around the knee joint, usually caused by too much kneeling. What, you might ask, has this got to do with gay sex?

Use your imagination.

Hunk

We all have our own idea of what or who is a hunk. For some people Jason Donovan fits the bill, but for others he is not big enough, tough enough or threatening enough. For them only Dolph Lundgren will do.

Hunks have three main characteristics: they are generally tall, well-built, and good-looking. The third characteristic is optional for some people, a brutish, heavy set and threatening face. No-one could call Arnie Schwarzenegger pretty, but he's definitely a hunk.

In the old days, Hunks used to be called beefcake, and how fashions change. Recently a series of the old Tarzan films were shown on television, and it was possible to make a comparative study of the development of the image of male glamour over the past sixty years. Starting with Johnny Weismuller, it became clear that people in the 1930s weren't averse to a bit of extraneous fat in their muscle-men – and Johnny could hardly have been called handsome. But he certainly wore the sexiest loin-cloth of them all. Then on through Lex Barker, who combined muscle and strength with a reasonable face, to Gordon Scott who was both pretty and sculpted – the precursor, indeed, of the present craze for rather artificially inflated strippers who look as though they spend as much time titivating and admiring themselves as they do seducing. I just can't imagine running my hands through the hair of a Chippendale – he'd be furious about having it mussed up!

IMPOTENCE

Impotence – failure to get or maintain an erection – can have devastating effects on some men. A doctor writing in the *British Medical Journal* described it thus: "Self-esteem plummets, self-anger and self-recrimination rage. Intimacy becomes a time of acute anxiety to be avoided. Embarrassment and poor communication still generally preclude early discussion of the difficulty."

Figures reported from the US showed approximately 10 million men suffer from some form of impotence. Each year this results in nearly 400,000 visits to outpatients clinics and 30,000 hospital admissions.

Some doctors think that the vast majority of cases of impotence are psychological in origin, while others insist that there are often physical causes. Naturally, men who are having problems with erections will prefer to believe that it is a mechanical rather than a "hang-up" problem, which is why those who promise instant "cures" are so popular.

There are, of course, some medical conditions, like diabetes, which can affect the ability of sufferers to get erections. Although it is well known that diabetes obstructs arterial blood supply, which can damage the feet, kidneys, eyes and heart, it isn't so well known that it can also interfere with blood flow to the penile arteries.

For those men whose impotence is caused primarily by blood flow problems of one kind or another, surgical intervention by a vascular surgeon might help. For those who are suffering from chronic impotence, which they have been unable to overcome through therapy or other treatment, it may be possible to have implants which will give an erection.

There are two types of prosthetic available, the first is an ingenious inflating device. Pump-up cylinders made of inert material are surgically implanted into the penis and then connected to a fluid reservoir implanted into the abdominal wall and a pump located in the scrotal sac. When an erection is desired, the man pumps fluid into the penile cylinders. When he has finished, he deflates the penis using the pump in his scrotum. The second method is a simple insertion of rods of inert material into the pressure chambers of the penis.

Both these devices can go wrong, of course, requiring more surgery to correct them. It all becomes extremely expensive as it is unlikely you'd be able to get such surgery on the NHS. The implants also permanently damage the pressure chambers in the penis, meaning that you can never have a natural erection after the operation.

Less drastic treatment is offered by some clinics which advertise widely in the press.This involves injecting into the penis a plant-based drug called papaverine, which is used to make blood vessels dilate. Each time the patient wants to have sex he has to inject himself with the drug, which means that sex can never be spontaneous: it requires about 15 minutes notice (which is how long the drug needs to take effect).

But Gordon Williams, a urologist at the Hammersmith Hospital in West London has his doubts. He conducted tests which showed that only seven per cent of his patients could be "kick-started" in this way. Like most conventional practitioners, he believes the majority of cases of impotence have psychological origins.

See also Erection.

INCOMPATIBILITY

This is a word much-favoured by those couples who've tried to make a go of it and failed. "We're incompatible" they say, "let's split". What it generally means is that one of them wants to have sex more often than the other. "He's oversexed" says one. "No, it's you – you're under-sexed" counters the other. But these are judgmental and meaningless terms. There is no "correct" number of times that we "should" have sex, no "normal" frequency. We have it when we feel like it. And if one feels like it and the other doesn't, what's wrong with having a wank? Or negotiating little safer sex adventures outside the relationship?

Just as a matter of interest, the *Journal of Homosexuality* in the USA surveyed 128 male gay couples to find out "how often they had genital sex with each other over the past month." 43% reported having sex less than twice a week; 27% said two to three times a week; 30% indicated more than three times a week. Needless to say, the couples that had been together longest had sex least frequently. Anyone who is trying to make a gay relationship work should accept that it changes quite radically over the years, and one of the most noticeable changes is the desire for sex. At the beginning it is likely to be frequent – very frequent. As the months and years move on, the frequency will decline quite rapidly. But this change may happen at a different pace for each partner, and so one might still be hot to trot twice a week, while the other would like to reserve it just for the occasional Sunday morning. The relationship need not end because of this difference in desire – don't be too quick to label it "incompatibility" and imagine it's all over bar the shouting. There are alternatives.

INFANTILISM

Playing at babies (autopaedophilia) is a sexual variation that is only just coming out of the closet, but it seems to be quite popular. The idea is that some people get a thrill from dressing up in nappies, having a dummy, and being confined to a cot. They are then comforted by their partner, who plays mummy (or daddy) or strict nanny, changing their nappy, giving them a breast feed (which even daddy can do during this particular fantasy), spanking them if naughty and sometimes even interfering with them in a way that would have the NSPCC jumping up and down if it weren't just make-believe.

Adult babies say that they like the combination of cuddles, domination and sado-masochism which it all involves. Naughty children must be smacked – sometimes with a cane – and nice children must be rewarded, by stroking and tickling and sometimes wanking.

Like all fetishes, this one can be pretty boring if it's an absolute essential element of every sexual encounter. But just occasionally it might be fun.

Infatuation

Being in love with someone who doesn't love you back is a painful enough experience at the best of times, but for young, isolated and inexperienced gay men, there is the added temptation of falling in love with an unsuspecting straight man. It's a common enough scenario. Young gays who haven't yet found their way on to the scene, where they might meet someone who would reciprocate their passion, can become fixated on male work colleagues, teachers or other people they come into contact with. Often these infatuations are secret, and the gay person who is worshipping from afar might construct elaborate fantasies involving their love-object.

Loneliness is a powerful emotion that can lead us into behaving foolishly and, I'm afraid, these infatuations seldom come to anything. Straight men might occasionally think they'd like to try gay sex, and sometimes they do, but they don't want to make a lifestyle out of it. And so, if you're in love with that gorgeous straight guy in accounts or that dashing hunk of a P.E. teacher, but he doesn't know about it (and neither does his girlfriend), you're saving up a lot of pain and disappointment for yourself.

But, I suppose, only by enduring and experiencing this pain can we learn lessons about survival in what can be a hard world. If you want to avoid this particular trauma, repeat this mantra ten times a day: I will not fall in love with straight men...I will not fall in love with straight men...

Infibulation

Back at the turn of the century masturbation was blamed for just about everything. It was considered a moral outrage, and every effort was made to discourage it among the young. Dirty-minded parents, worried by tales of blindness, moral turpitude and weakening of the brain, tried everything to keep their young sons from playing with themselves. They tied up their hands at night, stapled their foreskins together, invented devices which prevented erections or made them very painful. This was infibulation – preventing sexual activity by piercing the penis with a steel pin or attaching steel splints to the genitals to prevent arousal. Chastity belts with locks on were one way of keeping hand away from chopper, and "alarums" were also popular – when a young man got an erection during the night, a bell would ring in his parents' room, causing them to rush in to make sure he wasn't being dirty under the duvet. But young men were resourceful. Love knows no locksmiths, as the old quotation tells us, and indeed, wanking cannot be stopped simply by locking the equipment away. Eventually it would have to be released, and then it would be business as usual.

Infidelity

Infidelity doesn't have quite the same kind of importance in gay life as it does in the heterosexual equivalent. Gay partners, even those who stay together over long periods, are statistically unlikely to be monogamous. Sexual adventures outside the primary partnership are, of course, common among heterosexuals, too; the difference is that *we* don't generally consider it a divorcing matter.

Some gay men who are in committed relationships have decided, perhaps because of fears of HIV, that they will try to keep their partnership monogamous. Sometimes they succeed, and sometimes they have to admit that such an arrangement doesn't suit them. It's a matter of choice and negotiation, and there are no marriage vows which forbid such flexibility for gay couples. So, that's one up to us, boys.

One study of 150 gay couples found that after five years together, not a single one of the partnerships was still monogamous.

Inhibitions

Nobody likes to admit that they are shy or unsure about their sexual activities. It's almost like an admission of failure to have to say to an ardent lover: "Do you mind – I don't like doing that, it makes me feel sick." Or wanting to have sex with the lights out because of uncomfortable feelings about the shape of our body or some other perceived imperfection. Often, people are inhibited by imaginary flaws, the most frequent of which is insecurity about the size of their penis. It's amazing how many men are discomfited by having to undress in communal circumstances, such as showers or changing rooms; they have become convinced that their cock is much too small while everyone else's is "the normal size". The fear is, of course, that what they see as a tiny tool will become the subject of ridicule. What man can imagine anything more humiliating than have his dick derided in public?

Of course when they're totally in repose, few penises could be described as impressive. Some dicks, which are nicely sized when erect, shrivel away to next to nothing when they're flaccid. And even when they're at full stretch, they're unlikely to be much more than six to six and half inches long. Anything over that is unusual, and the owner is likely to be either a porn star or, at least, very popular. The possession of a bigger-than-average cock is simple good luck. Most of us have to make up for the lack of inches in other ways.

Inhibitions about sex can also be frustrating. Men who have not totally come to terms with their sexual orientation often have difficulties with certain activities. Some don't like sucking because they see it as "dirty", others don't like kissing because it's "unmanly", others don't like having their tits touched because they think it's "women's stuff".

Men who are inhibited about their bodies, or about certain elements of homosexual sex, need a lot of reassurance. If they find the right lover who will encourage them to open up, and it will help them enjoy their sex lives more.

INSEMINATE

This simply means 'to squirt semen into'. These days the only thing the sensible gay man squirts semen into is a condom.

Some gay men have agreed to help lesbians inseminate themselves by donating sperm (which is produced by wanking), although anyone contemplating this should think carefully about the issues around being a father and what part, if any, you intend to play in the child's life.

INTER-FEMORAL SEX

Literally, fucking between the thighs – once called 'slicklegging'. It is a popular alternative to penetrative intercourse. The person on the receiving end simply crosses his feet, which pushes the thighs together. The active person can then force his chopper between the thighs and shags away. Naturally this is more comfortable with plenty of lubrication. Hairy legs can also make for a scratchy experience.

INTIMACY

What's lacking from much casual gay sex is intimacy, the closeness, giving and vulnerability that makes sex such a wonderful experience. It isn't easy to open yourself up emotionally with a partner you may only have met minutes previously, and therefore the encounter may be robbed of a communicative dimension. Those who prefer only non-committed gay sex, and who avoid any kind of attachment to their partners can often lose out. An element of affection certainly adds that extra *je ne se quoi* to love-making.

INVERT

This was one of the first word used to describe homosexuals way back in the nineteenth century. Until then it had been generally assumed that men fucked women and anyone who deviated from that was simply buggering about. Later it was recognised by people like Edward Carpenter and the early sexologist Havelock Ellis, that some people's whole orientation was inclined towards members of their own sex, so a new word was needed to describe it. "Invert" is what they came up with.

ITALIANS

Here I must allow a note of personal preference to enter into the proceedings. I have travelled to every European country in my time, and I have to admit that although all of them have beautiful men, Italy has by far and away the biggest proportion of head-turners. Walk down any street in any Italian town and you will be struck by the extreme beauty and grace of many of the men. And, yes, I know about the vest-wearing, unshaven slobs who eat too much spaghetti and abuse Sophia Loren in old movies, but I am talking numbers here.

One of the most appealing aspects of an Italian holiday is sitting on the piazza of some pavement cafe, sipping that incredible coffee and watching not the world, but the waiters, go by. It's like a beauty contest, and every one of them has an arse to drool over. They invariably wear those tiny, waitery waistcoats and tight black trousers that accentuate every nook, cranny and crevice. And the swaggering machismo of the Latins is as attractive as it is repellent. *Bella*!

And *grazie* to all those youthful Roman scooter riders who sit with their legs apart on their machines – what a treat to the foot-weary tourist. Just keep your thieving hands off my camera, that's all. *Ciao* also to the Italian football players who are making such an impact on television. I am about as interested in football as I am in page three of *The Sun,* but I have become an avid viewer of the games featuring Juventas, Roma and Lazio – the men in these teams are seriously swarthy. Who wouldn't like to a fly on the wall of their changing room?

ITHYPHALLIC

If the modern gay community seems to be preoccupied with pricks, it can't hold a candle to ancient Rome, where they literally worshipped cock. The Ithyphallus was the ceremonial cock which was carried at Bacchic festivals, and if you've seen Derek Jarman's film *Sebastiane*, you'll have observed the whole thing in motion. Remember the sequence at the beginning when Lindsay Kemp and his troupe of dancers romp about, equipped with huge wooden cocks? That was Ithyphallus. It also refers to any lewd behaviour, and is the metre for poetry of a lascivious nature.

Jacking off

Jacking off or jerking off is an American expression for wanking. As American sexual mores are as ubiquitous in this country as their hamburgers, I shall fly the British flag and place this subject under W.

However, it is interesting to consider where the expression "jacking off" came from. Some people think it might be a shortening of the word "ejaculation", but more likely it is a slightly more polite way to say "jerking off", the origin of which which doesn't take a great deal of imagination.

Jail sex

French writer Jean Genet is the man who popularised the idea that sex between rough and ready jail inmates is glamorous. In his books (particularly *Our Lady of the Flowers*) and his much-banned short film *Un chant d'amour* (which, by the way, is now available, uncensored, on video in the Gay Classics series) the theme of love in prison recurs over and over.

Any institution which forbids its inmates access to the opposite sex will find that homosexuality rapidly becomes an important part of its ethos. So it is with jails. All these young men banged up together, with their testosterone running riot and no outlet except the occasional hand-job – what can you expect other than they'll turn to each other for comfort and relief?

And since Genet released it, it has become a common gay fantasy, too. All these straight men with rampant libidos, desperate to unload, and you only too happy to help the poor souls in their hour of need. The problem is that reality is not very often like the fantasy. There are too many anguished accounts of what life is like in prison for men who are considered pretty to be under any illusion that it's a pleasure trip. Rape, coercion, internal injuries and lethal jealousies are the unfortunate facts of the matter. I am sure that there must have been love affairs in prison, but these are few and far between and would not be well tolerated by the other prisoners, who would be happy to sexually abuse men weaker than themselves, but would not allow those same men to be the subject of loving friendship from anyone else. They will relieve themselves on fellow prisoners, but loving them is regarded as "sick.". Part of Genet's fascination with prison sex was, of course, its brutality.

It is also well-known that the warders will often abuse prisoners sexually, and this may be why they are known as "screws". Still, in the world of fantasy – particularly in porn videos where variations on *Un chant d' amour* are common – it's usually humpy young men waiting until the lights are out before going at it as though there was no tomorrow.

Jamming

Jamming is a very interesting variation for those of an experimental frame of mind. You need to buy a pair of outsize boxer shorts, really the largest size you can find. Then both you and your lover get into them, either face-to-face or back to front, depending on what your preference is, and commence having extremely intimate sex. Being jammed together so closely does restrict movement, but this somehow makes the whole thing much more *deliberate* and therefore much more sexy. A lot more effort is required to get the stimulation you want, and the resultant thrashing about can create an electrifying atmosphere of sheer lust. Of course, you might find that cheaper underwear will tear and let you down. It's worth paying that little extra for this particular experience.

Jealousy

Most of us know the depressing feelings that go with jealousy – the lumpen weight in the stomach, the agitation, the suspicion, the inability to sleep or eat properly. Sexual jealousy is a poisonous emotion which can lead us a not-so-merry dance.

Despite the politically correct dictum that jealousy has no part in gay relationships, our inconvenient emotions tend to be unreconstructed. Statistically there are very few gay couples that remain totally faithful to one another (see Infidelity); often they agree that they will have romantic adventures outside their primary relationship. In theory, this is a satisfactory arrangement. But what happens when one partner turns out to be more successful than the other at attracting extra partners? What happens when one lover thinks it's OK for him to sleep around but can't bear the thought of his partner in someone else's arms?

If you feel possessive about your lover, to the degree that you constantly suspect that he is being "unfaithful", then the odds are that you are feeling quite insecure. Depending totally on someone else to provide the meaning in your life is asking for disappointment. Which is not to say that you should feel guilty about jealous feelings, you should simply try to get them under control. How do you manage that?

Simple – you find yourself other support systems and friendships away from the primary relationship. In that way you won't be totally destroyed if you discover that your lover doesn't imagine you're the *only* person in the world.

JEANS

These cotton twill trousers were originally invented as a hard-wearing work garment in the wild west of America. I don't suppose Mr Levi Strauss, a Bavarian immigrant to California in 1850, who invented jeans, ever imagined that they would become the most popular item of clothing of the twentieth century.

Strauss saw a market for hard-wearing clothing among the gold miners of the time, and began to make trousers from the tent canvas he was selling. He soon realised that he needed an even tougher fabric for the job and this he found in France. It was called *serge de Nîmes* (hence denim). He dyed this a deep, uniform indigo and stitched and riveted it into sturdy pants that could withstand anything the cowboys and gold miners could throw at it. Through every generation since they were invented, denim jeans have never gone out of fashion.

Perhaps because of their association with rough, tough, working men, jeans were taken up by the gay crowd, who refined (and tightened) the design.

There were all kinds of ways of making jeans emphasise the positive. It was once necessary to sit in a bath of water while wearing them in order to shrink them into a sort of second skin. Other men would scour the crotch area with match-box ends in order to make the material there thinner and a different colour. This gave emphasis where it was desired.

More worldly designers have since put the ribbing and studs, which were originally meant to strengthen the jeans, to good use. Nowadays the ribbing in the back often pulls the jeans up the crack of the arse. You can also buy pre-ruined jeans with rips, holes and tears in all the most provocative places.

JOCK ITCH

Also sometimes known as 'jock rot' or 'dhobie itch', the official name for this unpleasant condition is Tinea Cruris, a fungal infection of the groin. It is caused by the wearing of tight pants – especially ones made from rubber and Lycra-style materials. Sweat cannot evaporate properly and the result is severe itching and redness in the crotch and on the scrotum. Get treatment from your doctor.

JOCK STRAP

The jock-strap is familiar to most gay people if only from its ubiquitous presence in gay advertising. Originally the "athletic support" was developed in the 19th century to protect cyclists from the bumps they experienced on the cobbled streets of the time. It went on to become a protective garment for sportsmen who needed to shield their knackers during violent contact games.

This was not the case in ancient Greece, where gymnasts (*gymnos* means "naked") relied on nature's very own protective device – the scrotum. It seems that when we are exercising, the cremaster muscles of the scrotum tighten, supporting the testicles and stopping them moving; meanwhile the spermatic cord, which links each testicle with the lower abdomen, pulls them upwards towards the body out of harm's way.

Naturally because it is associated with youthful male genitalia, the jock strap soon became the subject of erotic attention. Leaving, as it does, the arse totally exposed, its design has a particular appeal to gay men. Here was everything the horny homosexual could desire in a single piece of clothing – a bulging basket of goodies at the front and an erotic emphasis to the rear.

Soon after its introduction, the jock-strap had become a fetish object in its own right. Young men who had never been on a football field or seen an athletics track were posing in night-clubs in jock-straps. There is even a trade in "used jockstraps". Men buy other mens' used and unwashed "athletic supports" in order to sniff the concentrated aroma of maleness which, over a few sweaty sessions, has collected in the pouch area. If the jock-strap has been used for masturbation purposes and, as a result, is crusty, with yellow stains, so much the better.

Many gay men like to make jock-straps part of their love play. One friend of mine says that he is so excited by the idea of a well-filled jock strap that he has been known to spend up to an hour playing with his partner's bulge before even allowing him to take the garment off.

Jodhpurs

Jodhpur is a town in India, and it was here, during the days of the British Raj, that jodhpurs were invented. These trousers are worn mostly by polo players and other people connected with horses. They are tight around the calf but then suddenly balloon out around the upper thigh. They look ridiculous at first sight, but their whiteness and the tightness of the crotch area will make them much more appealing on closer inspection. Jodhpurs are generally associated also with riding crops and black boots.

Unfortunately, jodhpurs are most likely to be worn by some grotesque (even if gorgeous) Hooray Henry type of person. But that doesn't mean that the polo uniform couldn't be put to use in sexual scenes. I suppose someone might be turned on by the idea of a good horse-whipping from the local squire. Especially if he's twenty-five, built like a tank and has more in common with his horse than simply polo-playing.

Group to contact:

- Boots and Breeches Club, PO Box 1465, Eastbourne, Sussex BN22 9QP.

Jogging

One survey revealed that men out jogging think about sex once every fifteen seconds. It is, therefore, worth remembering when you see that humpy number running down your road in his extremely brief shorts and singlet, he has, at almost any given moment, got a sexual image in his mind. If you think that the sex he is pondering is your sort of sex, it might be worth your while "accidentally" tripping him up, and then offering to rub Sloane's liniment into any part that is aching (which, if you're lucky, will turn out to be his upper, inner thigh).

You could try to pass yourself off as a physiotherapist at the local jogging club and offer your services free to those men requiring hand relief after a hard morning's running round thinking dirty thoughts.

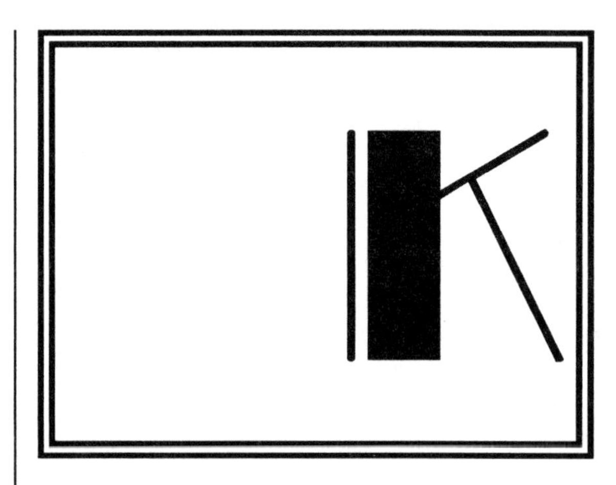

Kilt

If you are not a Scotsman, then technically you aren't entitled to wear a kilt. But if you are turned on by the idea of appearing in public with everything hanging free, just out of sight, then a kilt might be the thing for you. Change your name to Mr McDick for the day. You can hire extremely fine and smart kilts, complete with all the accompanying paraphernalia, from most dress hire shops. You will then have to master the technique, already second nature to women, of sitting down without putting everything on show. (Or otherwise – depending on your motive for wearing the kilt in the first place.)

For those unused to wearing the kilt, the sporran might prove to be a bit of a nuisance. As you walk along it bounces up and down on the naughty area and may cause unwanted erections in the over-excitable. The sporran should always contain a safe sex kit as the kilt has been known to inflame the passions of complete strangers, and it's as well to be prepared.

Group to contact:

- The International Kilt Appreciation Society - a gay social and contact group for the wearers/admirers of kilts can be found care of Mervyn Tacy, 'Ziveli', 20 Ordsall Park Road, Retford, Notts DN22 7PA. Please enclose a stamped addressed envelope when writing.

KISSING

The continental habit of kissing each other briefly on each cheek seems to have spread through the gay community like wildfire. Everywhere you go these days, people are calling you darling and brushing their faces against yours. I have to say that it makes me very uncomfortable – I'm just not a kissy-kissy sort of person. It always looks charming and completely natural in, say, a French village market-place, but not at all right in the basement of some grotty gay club.

I recognise that this attitude is very English and I shall try to overcome it. In Tudor times kissing was an accepted greeting in England, as the philosopher Erasmus noted: "Wherever you go in Britain everyone welcomes you with a kiss...turn where you will, there are kisses, kisses everywhere".

The English revulsion to the idea of men kissing each other seems to have begun in the eighteenth century. In 1749 the author of a book called *Satan's Harvest Home* said that male kissing was an example of the effeminacy which was more associated with Italians, and was liable to end up in sodomy. A German travel book of 1819 warned visitors to England that "The kiss of friendship between men is strictly avoided as inclining towards the sin regarded in England as more abominable than any other."

Sexual kissing – sometimes called snogging – is an essential element in intimate liaisons. The lips are extremely sensitive (indeed, there are more nerve fibres going from the soma sensory cortex in the brain – where sensations of touch are received – to the lips than to any other part of the body, including the hands and genitals), so there is little wonder that there is so much pleasure to be gained from pressing them together with those of our partner.

The kiss is usually a good indication that something pleasant is going to happen between the two people involved. A research team at the University College, London recently published the results of a comprehensive survey of kissing. They discovered that a special set of muscles – one of 20 such groups around the mouth – are squashed into a J-shape when we kiss. Only human beings are able to form their mouths into the necessary pout. Dr Henry Gibbons described mouth to mouth kissing as: "The anatomical juxtaposition of two orbicularis oris muscles in a state of contraction."

But kissing has become something of an art form, surrounded by mythology and anxiety. Agony aunts receive many letters from worried teenagers who are convinced that they don't know how to kiss. "Tell me how to do it," they say in a blind panic. They are horrified that when it comes to the crunch they won't get it right and their lack of experience in this important art will cause them to be laughed at by their contemporaries.

French kissing specifically worries them. Are you supposed to put your tongue into your partner's mouth, and if so how far? they ask. And what if the prospect of having someone else's spit on your tongue makes you want to heave?

Well, you either like French kissing (or deep kissing or wet kissing) or you don't, and if you don't, why feel obliged to do it? If someone is probing at your cakehole area, which is clamped shut because you don't want them exploring your oral cavity with that slimy old tongue of theirs, then it seems perfectly acceptable for you to keep your gob shut and not feel guilty about it.

If you *do* like it wet and soggy, though, just open wide and let him in. There is something uniquely *abandoned* about licking out each other's mouths. When he's shown you how it's done, do it back.

The down side to kissing is that the mouth is probably home to more kinds of nasty bugs and bacteria than any other part of the body. French kissing is an easy way to pass on infections. Colds, flu, sore throats and glandular fever love French kissers. HIV, however, is not one of those infections easily transmitted by this route. Analysis has shown that the virus which can lead to Aids is not present in saliva in sufficient quantity to make it a very great risk. No-one can say for sure that there is no risk whatsoever, but there is scant evidence to show any connection between deep kissing and HIV infection. So long as both your mouths are healthy, you shouldn't worry too much.

Of course, the mouth is not the only part of the body that can be kissed. Anywhere is good for either a quick peck or longer oral attention.

Here is a little exercise you can do to improve the shape and strength of your lips: open your mouth as if to yawn, lower the jaw slowly, moving the corners of your mouth inwards. Lips and surrounding areas will feel taut, use fingers to hold chin down, stretch top lip outwards while keeping mouth in an oval shape, hold for a count of five. Repeat three times a day.

Fascinating fact:

- In the forties there was a craze for "sparks parties", at which the participants should wipe their feet on nylon carpets until they had generated a fair amount of static electricity. Then they would turn the lights out and watch the sparks fly as they kissed each other.

KNEE TREMBLER

A fifties expression for hurried sex, usually performed standing up. Knee tremblers are usually enjoyed in some public place where the chance of discovery is ever-present. It has to be done quickly, therefore, and with as little disturbance to clothing as possible. Heterosexuals were famed for having knee tremblers in shop doorways, while gay men had to find more discreet places such as dark alleyways and loo stalls. In Germany a knee trembler is called *knieziterrer*; in Spanish a *trembla rodillero* and in French a *baiser debout*.

For those wishing to take up S&M in a big way, the ability to tie a variety of knots will become quite important. Many will have mastered this – as well as many other pertinent skills – during their time in the boy scouts. However, once a taste has been developed for bondage, the tying of ever more elaborate knots will be necessary. You will need to know all about slip knots, reef-knots and nooses.

For those who are heavily into tying people up, many happy hours can be spent in inventing new ways of harnessing the slave.

Tying people to beds is most popular, although those who have a fully equipped dungeon will also have other methods – hitching-posts, hooks and pulleys will be available for those who want to go as far as they can go with ropes and knots.

- Fascinating fact: there are more than 4,000 different kinds of knots, so plenty of studying to do.

This is a psychiatric condition where sufferers become convinced that their genitals are shrinking. Their conviction becomes so intense that they may take extreme measures to stop the process – like attaching weights to their penis. It isn't very common among British gay men, but there are about 2,000 cases a year in America

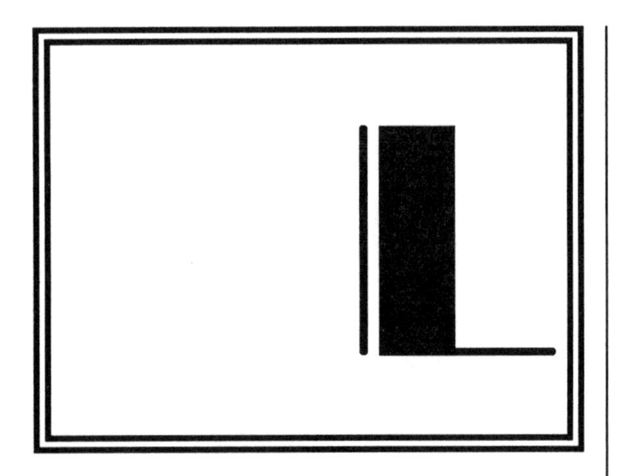

Laughter

Laughter might not seem such an essential element in good sex, but if you can incorporate a bit of light-hearted fun into your love-making you'll find it so much more satisfying. I know it isn't always possible to be jokey when you're with someone new, and feeling nervous and apprehensive about what is going to happen. You may be anxious to give a good impression or not want to risk being misunderstood. Most men are nervous about their sexual performance and an inappropriate laugh at the wrong moment can make even the firmest erection behave like a collapsing factory chimney.

However, longer-term lovers can allow a bit of slap and tickle and a few private jokes in bed without offence being taken. When you're relaxed enough with your lover to be able to feel the bed rocking with laughter as well as humpty, then you can be sure that you've established that special trust that means so much (see also Disasters).

Leash

Dog leashes and collars are very popular among S&M aficionados. The master puts it on his slave and then leads him around like a pet who is in sore need of rescuing by the RSPCA. It's a common form of ritual humiliation which has become a little passé since Madonna was seen to do it in public. But, if that's what you like – then, woof-woof.

Leather

Leather is the oldest known material to be used as clothing for human beings. Even back in the stone age they were wearing Mammoth hide to keep out the cold – and perhaps even using it to make leather cock rings for all we know.

More recently leather has become the number one fetish in the gay community. Everybody loves a bit of the black, shiny stuff, especially if it is adorning a biker or other well-built gentleman who can do it justice. A whole culture has grown up around the wearing of leather, and much effort is put into the design of garments which show it, and the wearer, off to best advantage. Consequently you have leather vests, leather pants, leather straps, gloves, jackets, hats, chaps and harnesses, jock-straps leather whips and even leather teddy bears.

I'm not sure how leather came to be associated with the homo-erotic, but I think Marlon Brando might have had something to do with it. In his earlier films, when he was a hunk you'd die for, he was often seen in leather caps or trousers. The "second skin" aspects of leather might also be appealing, and there is little doubt that the best leather garments stretch and reveal in a most satisfying manner.

- A catalogue of leather and other fetish clothing can be had from Fantasy Erotique, 7 Disraeli Road, London E7 9JR. Tel: 0181-555 2996.
- Rob, 24/25 Wells Street, London W1

Lewd, lascivious, lubricious

Lewd behaviour means behaving sexually in ways that other people might consider beyond the pale. A lewd person is far from shy when it comes to sexual practices, and if you meet someone who is anxious to show you some new tricks in bed, then you've met a lewd. And lucky old you.

"Lewd" is one of the many words which the nutty anti-sex brigade have invented in order to make inventive or unusual sex sound undesirable. I think it is time that we reclaimed the word, together with all the others which they use to insult the sexually unconventional among us. Just as we've taken back "queer" and detoxified it, so we should give other sex-words a more positive meaning. After all, what's wrong with a bit of lewdity as long as it is between consenting adults? It sounds like a whole lot of fun to me. So, I am now formally suggesting that we grab back the following delightful words: lewdity, indecency, outrageousness, licentiousness, dirtiness, filthiness, smuttiness, sleaziness, salaciousness and lubricity. After all, they represent those legendary "good things in life" which are free (for the most part, anyway). And if some people don't like it, they can bugger off – although such a course of action would probably be wasted on them.

I am particularly anxious that *lubricious* should become our word because it has such a wonderfully dirty, smutty sound to it. It actually means slippery and slimy as well as lewd and rude, so it's a good all-purpose word for the kind of sex we all like most.

Just let "lubricious" roll around your mouth, like a fine old wine. It has a distinctly fruity taste and holds the promise of all kinds of delirious pleasures to follow.

Libido

Libido is our sex drive, the impetus that makes us want sex in the first place. Like other bodily cycles, it has its highs and lows. If we are off sex for a while – and sometimes it happens even to the randiest of us – we say that our libido is low. It's almost heretical for some men to admit that sometimes they just aren't in the mood, can't be bothered, or want to go to sleep. But, if we're being honest, that is how it is from time to time for all of us.

A lot of men have problems admitting that the strength of their libido fluctuates over a period of time, they feel that they will be exposing themselves to ridicule if they aren't seen to be sexually available at all times. Some are so bound up in this macho trap that they see it as an admission of failure if the opportunity for sex is there, but there is no desire to take it.

Lots of things can affect our desire for sex at any given time. Stress is numero uno. If we're having a bad time in life, perhaps through unemployment, broken relationships, illness, bereavement or whatever, the desire for sex might disappear altogether for a period. It's no big deal. Given time, things will right themselves naturally.

At the other end of the scale, of course, there are periods when our libido is running rampant, and we're ready for sex at just about any time of day or night – sometimes we want it several times a day, and it can be a darned nuisance not being able to think about anything else until we've de-spunked.

For what it's worth, my advice is to listen to what your body is telling you and go with it. Don't let anxiety about the off-periods make life miserable. (See also under Impotence and Erection).

Licking

The tongue is a particularly attractive sex toy. Not only is it extremely sensitive for its owner (as anyone whose ever accidentally bitten it will testify), its warm, wet probings are quite unlike anything else for those on the receiving end.

Like every other part of the body, tongues vary from person to person. Some people have incredibly long and agile tongues which they can poke out to prodigious lengths, others have discreet little things, which can, nevertheless, still provide hours of entertainment.

All parts of the body can be licked, but here is a list of the more traditional destinations for a tongue in erotic mode: lips; other tongues; ears; neck; armpits; fingers; nipples (and environs); abdomen; cock; balls; anus; buttocks; back of knees; toes and, for fans only, the bottom of the feet. The only drawback to licking is that sometimes the areas being attended to aren't as clean as they could be and, occasionally, long, choking pubic hairs are ingested. It's amazing how these have the capacity for sticking in the throat in a most uncomfortable manner.

We have already looked at licking food from your partner's body, but what about natural secretions? The taste of these vary from person to person – try comparing ear-wax from one man to the next, it's fascinating. Sweat, too, can range from the sweet and salty to the bitter and musty, depending on how recently it was produced. Licking is a nice occupation if you can be sure of no nasty surprises, so keep yourself clean and tasty and you'll not go far wrong.

There have been thousands of attempts to define Love and to separate it from its close cousin Lust. After all, love is the basis of Christianity but lust, we are told, is one of its seven deadly sins. There is still no foolproof formula for telling one from the other. It has been said of love that "you'll know it when you feel it," but this is misleading. Our old and welcome friend Lust can put on a very convincing disguise and pass himself off as Love very easily – there is a distinct family resemblance.

Love and Sex don't necessarily go together, but when they do, they produce a very different experience to that of Lust and Sex. I'm not making any judgements about which is "best" because I don't think such a judgement is possible – the experience is just different, that's all. Of course, there is a school of thought which says that really fantastic, ball-breaking sex is impossible for people who are in love. It takes a casual relationship – which does not involve a longer-term need to impress the partner – in order for true abandonment to take place. People who are in love will not want to spoil their chances of a longer-term commitment by sharing too many sexual secrets or demanding things that might otherwise compromise their standing in the eyes of the loved one. But casual lovers have only one thing in mind – the reaching of the best possible orgasm by the most interesting possible route. Their relationship is likely to end before boredom or resentment have time to develop, and before explanations of particular desires need to be proffered to a partner. If you happen upon someone who is prepared to indulge your every fantasy with no questions asked, and who you don't have to face in the morning, then – goes the thinking – mind-blowing sex is possible.

Being In Love, rather than In Lust (or 'on heat' as the more prosaic term it), means that you'll probably spend a lot of time thinking about the object of your affections. In the early stages of a love affair this can be almost obsessive. It is not unusual for the newly-in-love to ring each other at work six or seven times a day and to leave flirtatious little notes around the house for each other. This may be delightful for the participants, but can be quite nauseating for those who are not involved but are obliged to spectate.

It isn't unusual for the newly-in-love to go off their food, become insomniac, feel as though they're walking on air, be maniacally happy, neglect friends, and have sex with the love object at every opportunity. This early, extremely pleasant, stage of a long-term relationship has been given the label "limerence" by one researcher. He suggested that this ecstatic phase lasts, on average, between six and eighteen months. After that, real life sets in. The sex-madness calms down a little, and the loved-one's nasty habits begin to become apparent. At first you might have regarded his snoring as cute but, as the relationship progresses, you might begin to perceive it as irritating. But if you're truly in love, you'll cope, and you won't pack it in at the first indication that "limerence" has passed.

Long-term, loving relationships between men – for these purposes we'll define it as relationships with a commitment beyond sexual attraction – have a controversial history. We're told frequently by our detractors that it is 'impossible' or 'unnatural' or 'perverted' for two men to love each other in the way that a man and woman can. If we produce evidence that such love is possible then we are assured that it is only "pretend" or that it's doomed to be short-lived "because you're so promiscuous."

These negative ideas have been put about by our enemies who want to keep us away from each other, but they are lies. While it's true that some gay men *do* have problems sustaining relationships, it's not because gay relationships are "impossible", it's simply because we have been indoctrinated to believe that they are undesirable and *can't* work. We internalise these myths at an early age, and they can be extremely difficult to shake off.

Be assured: if you want to have a long-term, committed relationship, then it is perfectly possible to succeed. And don't be worried about the politically correct within our own community who say such arrangements are "unhealthy" because they ape heterosexual relationships which, in turn, are unbalanced and exploitative. What we feel in our heart of hearts is not subject to political correctness, so if the radicals don't like it, they can lump it.

Book to read:

- If you want to have a soul-mate, but you can't solve the problems that seem to sabotage your efforts at partnership, why not read my book *Making Gay Relationships Work* published by The Other Way Press, PO Box 130 London W5 1DQ.

LUBRICANTS

Men don't have quite the same juice-producing propensities as women, and so when two men make love together, they need a little something to help smooth the way. A whole range of lubricants have been employed over the ages. Vaseline, baby oil, butter (and margarine for those on social security), petroleum jelly, Nivea, Brylcreem, Mazola, soap – all have served to make gay love-making more comfortable.

Then came the ultimate sexual lubricant, K-Y Jelly. Thank you Johnson and Johnson for providing us with such an indispensable handy and useful sex aid. (It is thought that K. Y. were the initials of the pharmacist who developed this lubricant, although even Johnson and Johnson aren't sure what his or her name was.)

Lubricants are mainly used by gay men in anal intercourse, but some use them for wanking because they give a different sensation, as well as providing a disgusting, *lubricious* squelching noise, which some find aurally arousing.

K-Y now comes in tubes and sachets rather than tubs, thus ensuring that it remains relatively clean and untainted after being opened. The only problem with the tubes is that if, in the heat of excitement, you forget to put the cap back on, you might roll over on to it and end up with the whole bed smeared in K-Y, which is most uncomfortable on a cold night.

Oily substances are, of course, OK for any sexy activity which isn't going to involve condoms. A popular sport is to lay a tarpaulin, or other waterproof material, on the floor, strip yourselves naked, smear oil all over each other (I mean, really coat yourselves – cheapest supermarket vegetable oil is suitable for this) and then roll about together on the waterproof.

Many exciting and lewd positions can be tried, as well as uninhibited sexual massage. It can be followed by a communal shower where, if you're feeling particularly fruity, activities can be continued with even more variations possibie.

LYCRA

This extraordinarily sensuous material was invented in the sixties as underwear for women who needed a little "support" for their saggy bits. Since then, it's stretch-and-display qualities have been taken up by sports persons and the proprietors of sex-shops. First there were cycle shorts, then there were running shorts (immortalised by Linford Christie at the Olympic Games), and then there were all manner of other items of clothing – best kept for private moments or for wearing at selected night-clubs.

Lycra is wonderful if you have a fabby body with not an ounce of excess fat. But it is merciless on those who have eaten too many Mars Bars and drunk too many pints of lager (see Abdomen). For the sake of their own dignity, no-one over the age of twenty-two should be allowed to wear Lycra in public.

Machismo

Machismo is, of course, a Spanish word, used in Latin America to describe an exaggeratedly 'masculine' way of behaving. Macho men like to swagger about in tight trousers, assuming an arrogant air which often manifests itself in horrendous violence. They particularly like to slap women around, drink prodigious amounts of beer, compete with each other in suicidal car races and generally carry on like mental cases. It is not clear whether this urge to macho behaviour is a genetic trait that men are stuck with (think of it – football hooligans may be the victims of their genes!), or whether society instils in us the idea that our gender gives men the right to rule the world.

The very existence of gay men undermines all this rather pathetic posturing, though, and that is why macho straight men get so worried when they come across homosexuality. There is nothing in the world that frightens up-tight hetty men more than gayness. Maybe they find us so intolerable because they see something of their own true feelings in our behaviour. Maybe that is why they have this urge to attack, ridicule and occasionally kill us.

Machismo is mostly a straight phenomenon. There are butch gay men, of course, but that isn't the same thing at all. Machismo is a sort of insanity that drives heterosexual youths into stabbing each other in large numbers at Saturday night discos. Straight pubs and clubs are awash with violence and mayhem at the weekends, whereas the gay equivalents hardly ever see so much as a broken glass. Why should that be? What drives heterosexual men to such extremes of aggression? It can't just be the testosterone factor, because homosexual men have just as much of that hormone floating around and it doesn't generally impel us to destroy everything that doesn't please us.

This is my theory: straight men are caught in a trap, the macho trap. They are raised with the expectation that they must out-run, out-drink, and out-fuck their contemporaries. It becomes a case of humiliate or be humiliated in front of your peer group, and humiliation is the one thing that a macho man cannot tolerate. This becomes an obsession. They go around with their "mates" – the only people they respect –

reinforcing each other's braggadocio. On their own they might be open to reason, in a gang they become insufferable.

Straight men, on the whole, despise women. They tolerate them because they want sex, but few can make real relationships with them. This is apparent by the widespread physical and psychological abuse of wives and girlfriends. The proliferation of battered women's shelters is proof enough of that.

Machos will deny that they have a feminine side to their nature – indeed, if you dare to suggest it to them, they will probably put you in hospital for a week.

Gay men, on the other hand, have a different motivation. They don't want to kill their mates, they want to mate with them! Generally, gay men are good to women – ask many straight women and you can bet a pound to a penny that they'll tell you their best male friend is gay. Fag-hags (not a very pleasant term, but a useful one) know when they're on to a good thing and they treasure their gay buddies.

Some gay men, of course, don't like to have women around – simply because they aren't men. But it isn't hatred, just indifference.

Zsa Zsa Gabor summed it up when she declared: Macho isn't mucho.

On the Tahitian islands, gay men are respected and given a place in society as Mahu. Traditionally Mahu were servants to the chief, they were men who dressed as women and had sex with the Tahitian braves.

These days Mahu can be seen haunting the bars and docks of Viti Levu, entertaining visiting French sailors. They are still accepted as an integral part of island life, and many Tahitians consider the Mahu to be bringers of good luck. Approximately one in five families have a son whom they raise as a girl and who goes on to live as a woman.

MASSAGE

The word 'massage' is very flexible. Because it involves intimate handling of the body, massage has become, in some instances, a euphemism for sexual contact, especially that offered by prostitutes. In order to get round the law, rentboys often advertise themselves as "masseurs". When you get to their "massage parlour" (or they come to your hotel room – an 'out-call' as it is known) you will be offered even more euphemistic services: such as 'hand-relief' (masturbation); 'full body massage' (intercourse possible) and even 'breast relief' (in which the 'masseur' rubs his clients penis over his nipples until he comes). Naturally, spanking and b&d (q.v.) can also be passed off as forms of massage.

However, massage is not the exclusive domain of prostitutes; lovers can use it as a very sensual experience. You don't need certificates to enjoy spreading baby oil all over your partner's body and allowing your exploring hands to run around all over the place. One variation is to massage every part of the body while assiduously avoiding touching the genitals. This can create heightened excitement for both parties.

Make sure that your hands are warm before commencing. Strip your partner down, and strip down yourself if you feel comfortable doing so. Place a large towel on the bed or floor, or wherever this manipulation is going to take place. Grease your partner generously with baby oil and commence to rub his body with your hands. The pressure should be firm but pleasantly reassuring.

You should start with your partner laying face down and rub his back and shoulders. Then gently rub the neck, as this is where a great deal of tension accumulates. Pay a lot of attention to the small of the back. Then play with his buttocks, kneading and fondling them, perhaps slipping your fingers between to massage the crack.

Work your way down his legs, and spend a lot of time on the feet. Then he can turn over and you can massage the front of his legs, his chest, shoulders, and maybe his face and scalp. Whether you wish to straddle your partner during the massage will be entirely up to you. Much depends how long you want it to last, and what you anticipate the end result will be (e.g. you'll be offering hand/body etc. relief).

So long as you are gentle, and encourage your partner to tell you what he is enjoying and what he isn't, you should find that massage is a wonderful turn-on as well as being very relaxing.

When you have fully relaxed his body, you should change places and he can take a turn massaging you.

There are several books on the art of sensual massage if this is an area you'd like to explore more thoroughly.

MASTURBATION

This very common practice is filed under its more popular name 'Wanking'.

MOLLIE HOUSES

These were 18th century establishments in London (the Heavens of their era) catering for the gay clientele of the day. Often young men would dress up in women's clothes for the entertainment and gratification of the customers. Many pillars of the establishment were caught with their trousers down in Mollie Houses. I'm sure it would be no different if they existed today.

Paris had its equivalents. In the 19th century there was one in particular which became world famous. It was operated by *la mère des tantes* – 'mother of the queans' – an elderly ex-hustler who had been financially ruined by the revolution. He provided facilities for all classes of men, but the luxuriousness of the room allotted depended entirely on the amount paid. Any preference could be catered for, and with advance warning the streets of Paris would be scoured for hustlers and rent boys who could service very specialised tastes (see also Agents Provocateurs; Vere Street Scandal).

Monogamy

From the Greek word meaning 'alone' and 'marriage'. In gay circles it usually means having sex with only one person. Serial monogamy means being faithful to one person at a time.

There has been a lot of discussion about the value of monogamy for gay men. When the Aids crisis first began to develop it was mooted as the answer. If we all stuck to one partner, we were told, the virus could not spread. Unfortunately some people who fell for this one found at a later date – too late by then – that their partner was, in fact, infected. Safer sex is the answer to protecting yourself from HIV, although fewer partners also means that the odds against you meeting someone who is infected are reduced.

For some gay men, though, monogamy is the way they want to live their lives. It might be a 'moral' choice or one that springs simply from overwhelming love for their partner. Research, though, shows that very few gay relationships remain 'closed' over a longer period.

Project Sigma found that 57 per cent of those in relationships of less than five years standing were non-monogamous. After five years 72 per cent of the couples were living in 'open' relationships.

Another survey (*The Male Couple* – McWhirter and Mattison) found that none of the 156 couples which took part in the research were still monogamous after the first five years of their relationship.

Couples that regard themselves as established, but who do not have an exclusive sexual relationship often negotiate elaborate rules for their outside activities. Maybe they will agree that they won't cruise for other partners when they are out together, or they promise not to bring extra partners back to their shared home. Some couples agree not to talk about their bits on the side – others prefer to know what's going on. One couple I know agreed that if either of them saw people outside the primary relationship for sex, it would be for one time only, and never with mutual friends. Another couple allow outside sex only when they are on holiday abroad. They reason that there will be no threat to their relationship when foreign lovers are left behind.

Monopodophilia

This word describes those who like to have sex with one-legged partners. There was a small sensation back in the seventies when *Gay News* carried a personal ad for someone looking for "an above-knee amputee" for fun and games. Like all obsessions and fetishes, monopodophilia can be very boring if it becomes the be-all and end-all of a person's sex life. It can't do much for the partner, either, if he becomes aware that he is wanted only for his disability. Still, it takes all sorts, I suppose.

Mort douce

This translates quite literally as "sweet death" and is used in several sexual contexts. The most obvious is to describe someone who dies while having sex, but the more poetic usage is to describe that deliciously all-too-brief moment in orgasm when it seems we are losing consciousness.

Moustaches and beards

Facial hair is an exclusively masculine feature (except for a few unlucky exceptions) and, as such, holds great appeal for some gay men. Indeed, the clone or 'bear' looks would be incomplete without a moustache and/or beard. But beard-wearers should remember that facial hair does not have the same soft texture as head hair and so, if you're snogging with someone who isn't used to a hairy face, you might find that the beard irritates and prickles them. Maybe they are prepared to tolerate it, but as a possessor of facial fungus myself, I can confirm that people with sensitive skins can come out in a rash after a close encounter with a beard. Washing the beard with baby shampoo can soften it up a little, but if you've just trimmed it, it can feel like a thousand needles when it comes into contact with someone else's tender places.

Beards come in several styles, the two most popular being the carefully tended (or 'diplomat') that is always beautifully shaped and trimmed, the other is the ragged and scruffy sort (the 'folk-singer') which is just an excuse for the wearer to stay in bed for an extra ten minutes in the morning.

The idea that people who wear beards are hiding something (spots, a weak chin, a dark secret) is of course, wholly untrue. It is simply a myth created by those who cannot grow a decent beard themselves.

On the other hand, beards can be an excellent method of reshaping an unsatisfactory physiognomy or hiding scars. They also accentuate the eyes, making them look sexier. Beards can come and go with ease so you can get rid of them and regrow them at will. With a little forethought you can almost use them as a fashion accessory. When someone who has worn a beard for many years suddenly shaves it off, it can be traumatic for his loved ones who suddenly see someone completely different inhabiting the clothes of their lover, relative or friend.

Those gay men with fetishes about facial hair are turned on very quickly by beards and moustaches, and may even find the discomfort of having it rubbed on their private parts stimulating. There are as many, though, who find them utterly repulsive.

The important thing that tyro beard-wearers should bear in mind is the way food sometimes get caught up in their pride and joy. Always check your face after a meal – there's nothing worse than trying to make a big impression on someone only to have them tell you: "You've got Weetabix stuck in your beard."

Mr Right

We're all searching for Mr Right (aka Man of Your Dreams), but all of us have a different image of who he is, and what we want him for.

To some, Mr Right means the partner they are going to be able to live with for the rest of their lives, the one who will satisfy all their desires, make them feel good, support them when they're down, give them great sex on demand and probably be knock-your-eyes-out gorgeous with it.

For others, the search for Mr Right is purely sexual. They are looking for someone with the face of Mel Gibson, the torso of Marky Mark, the cock of Jeff Stryker, the legs of Arnold Shwarzenegger and the sex drive of a rutting stag (or any permutation of the above). They want this ideal man just for sexual gratification. The problem is that he probably doesn't exist (or if he does, chances are he wouldn't be interested). If nothing short of this fantasy will do, then sexual activity is likely to be fairly infrequent.

The search for Mr Right can be a pain, particularly if we have a picture in our minds of something very specific. Take a look at some of the personal ads in the gay press to see that many men are looking for an idealised partner which they are very unlikely to find. They are specific about hair-colour, age, height, and invariably they must be "hung" and inevitably "straight-acting" (the possession or otherwise of a foreskin also seems to be of overwhelming importance to some).

We all have preferences, and there's nothing wrong with that; they are a product of our history and our experiences. In real life, however, most of us have to compromise. We take what is offered rather than chasing fantasies. If you find what you're looking for, great. If you don't: well, make the most of what you can get!

Multiple Orgasm

It's been known for a long time that women can achieve multiple orgasms, but what about men? It has been traditionally thought that when a man has an orgasm, that's it – it's all over bar the shouting and he has to rest a while before he can go again. Many men find that it doesn't take very long to reach the ejaculatory stage once direct genital stimulation has begun.

But now researchers in America claim they have discovered that most men are born with the ability to experience multiple orgasms, and the skill lies in being able to control key muscle groups. This seemed too good to miss, and so for the benefit of readers I have thoroughly researched the theory.

According to the latest research project conducted by William Hartman PhD, a former president of the US Society for the Scientific Study of Sex, 12 per cent of men are naturally multi-orgasmic and most men can train themselves to be.

During multiple orgasmic intercourse, men achieve an orgasmic state within about 15 minutes. By controlling their muscles they can enjoy a state very close to ejaculation for 10 to 15 minutes until they experience actual ejaculation.

Ah, so male multiple orgasm isn't quite what we thought it was. We aren't going to suddenly turn our single-shot pistols into machine guns overnight. The telling point is "a state very close to" ejaculation. So, now we know what we're talking about, how's it done?

One way, according to Dr Hartman, is to wait until you feel that ejaculation is approaching and then squeezing the underside of the penis for fifteen seconds to halt the urge in its tracks. Alternatively, the man can deter ejaculation by using a finger to prevent the testicles from elevating fully (the testicles rise up close to the body during orgasm). The third method – which Dr Hartman terms "The Rolls Royce method" – involves consciously tightening the pubococcygeus (PC) muscle (the one that men use to stop the flow of urine midstream) for fifteen seconds. Ideally men should build up their PC muscle in order to perfect this technique. Try contracting the PC muscle for a three-second count then relaxing and repeating the exercise ten times. Follow this up with ten quick "flicks", tightening and relaxing the PC muscle in quick succession.

If you want to read more, get a copy of Dr Hartman's book *The Male Sexual Machine*.

However, British sexual counsellors are a little worried by the American emphasis on "performance sex". They feel that loving, caring and mutually reassuring sexual episodes are much more satisfying in the long run than acrobatic or consciously extended ones which require a lot of effort and which can cause anxiety if they don't work. Renate Olins of counselling organisation Relate says: "Orgasm doesn't necessarily make people ecstatic as partners. Ultimately the notion of the male multiple orgasm could cause more worry among men than pleasure."

So, it's up to you whether you want to pursue this particular dream (and there are many who are still sceptical about whether it is reality or fantasy and hype), but don't let it become an obsession which ultimately spoils, rather than enhances, your enjoyment of sex.

Mutual Masturbation

Wanking each other off is an extremely popular pastime with gay men. A large-scale research project into gay sex lives showed that 95 per cent of respondents had masturbated another man and 96 per cent had been masturbated by another man.

Mutual wanking is sometimes just *part* of a sex session, and sometimes it is an end in itself. It is certainly the easiest and most practical way to reach an orgasm in dangerous or restricted circumstances. It has the advantage, too, of being one of the safest of the safer sex activities.

You can wank your partner while standing behind him and reaching around him, you can do it while facing each other. You can do it one at a time or together. A friend of mine likes to kneel in front of his partner and wank him till he shoots a load all over his face. No wonder it's such a popular activity, it has just about everything going for it.

Mutual Orgasm

A lot of people think it is desirable for partners to climax together if they can. Personally I don't buy this idea. How can you concentrate on maximum enjoyment of the orgasm for yourself and your partner if you are both experiencing your morts douce at the same time? Much better, I think, to come in turn and make the most of it.

The argument in favour of mutual orgasm is that it might be difficult for the person who fired the first shot to maintain a sufficient level of interest after orgasm. That pesky old refractory period (q.v.) which occurs immediately after you've shot a load, often dictates a distinct loss of interest in any immediate further activities in the below-the-belt regions.

It's all a matter of personal taste.

NATIVISM

Nativism is the theory that homosexuality – and other sexual variations – stem from inborn rather than learned or conditioned influences.

There has been a lot of interest in this recently with three research projects seeming to suggest that there might be a genetic or hormonal influence on whether a person turns out to be gay. One suggested that the hypothalamus of gay men was smaller than that of straight men, and this might hold the answer. The researchers at the Salk Institute in America announced that they had discovered what they thought was a "gay gene", and there was a flurry of controversy when ex-Chief Rabbi Jakobovits said that he would be in favour of homosexuals being genetically screened out of existence.

Mary Whitehouse, the legendary "clean-up campaigner" and loony, had her own theory – expounded in her book *Whatever Happened to Sex?* – that homosexuality "is entirely precipitated by the abnormal (in terms of moral as well as physical norms) sexual behaviour of parents during pregnancy." I suppose anyone who can believe that the Bible is true in its entirety, as she does, can believe anything.

No theory that has yet been put forward can be said to be definitive and each has its scorning critics. There are those who feel that such research is sinister, with the ultimate aim of finding a "cure" for homosexuality, and those who are convinced that homosexuality is a "chosen" way of life that can be changed with psychotherapy or even prayer.

The sexologists Masters and Johnson will give those of their clients "with a strong motivation to change" all kinds of psycho-therapy. The Exodus organisation claims to "pray" you out of your lustful feelings for the same sex. In the fifties and sixties psychiatrists used electric shocks and emetics to put people off their sexuality. And a Viennese psychiatrist, Albert von Schrenk-Notzing (1862-1929), became noted for trying to change homosexual orientation by the use of hypnosis and visits to straight brothels for 'reconditioning'.

And yet, despite their cruelty and foolishness, we're still here, we're still queer and they can't do anything about it!

Necrophilia

Having sex with dead bodies could, I suppose, be said to be a morbid condition. The average necrophiliac is generally uninterested in other kinds of sex, although there are some prostitutes who will imitate a corpse for necrophiliac customers.

Nether eyebrow

This is a rather quaint 19th century euphemism for pubic hair.

Nibbling

Ear-lobes are particularly susceptible to nibbling, but gentle biting can be exciting on most parts of the body. So long as the skin is not broken it's OK to nibble to your heart's content. If you have a jagged tooth, though, be careful because those unintentional scratches can easily become infected.

Ninety-nine

99 (or, at a pinch, 66) signifies anal intercourse in the way that 69 indicates mutual fellatio.

Nipples

Why do men have nipples? This is the perennial question for those who have minds of an enquiring disposition. What are they for? Well, I now have the definitive answer, and it has nothing to do with developmental embryology as previously thought.

I have discovered that certain passages have been deleted from the Bible over the centuries, particularly those concerned with sex and nose-picking. These missing passages – hidden from history by anti-sex and anti-bogey religious maniacs – have recently come to light in a cave near Jerusalem. I have had the well-known biblical scholar J. Peesmold Grunt-Thuttock translate the scraps of parchment, which it is thought were left in the cave by ancient tribesmen who had used them for toilet paper. Here is the first draft of the translation which was blue-pencilled from the original Book of Genesis – concerning events in the Garden of Eden:

"And it came to pass that when Eve had eaten of the fruit of knowledge, she felt a great burning in her loins. She said unto Adam: Here, get your fig-leaf off, chuck, and douse my desire. And so Adam did as he was bade and they lay together and *knew* each other. Afterwards, as they smoked their ciggies, it came to pass that Adam was mighty puzzled by the fact that Eve had got a lot of pleasure from her chest regions – pleasure that for him had been denied. He called unto the skies, saying: Oh heavenly father – I am sorely puzzled as to why Eve should have them bumps on her chest and why she liked having them played with. And God sayeth unto Adam: Them are her titties, which she will need at a later date for other purposes. Neat aren't they? And Adam looked at his own chest, which was naked, except for a blackhead which had come up that day. How come I haven't got no titties? he asked. Why should she have all the fun?

And God said unto Adam: Alright, well you can have a couple of titties as well, but yours shall only have only one function, rather than two.

And so it came to pass that God gave Adam a couple of hot buttons, one on each side of his chest, and Adam found them mighty pleasant to play with."

It is obvious from this that nipples were put on men's chests as a sort of bonus extra by God the Father, rather in the way that Kellogg put free plastic dinosaurs in the Corn Flakes packets.

Experts are trying to authenticate the passages, but until they do, it's as good an explanation as any. Just be thankful we've got them.

Of course, pesky old scientists, have a different explanation that's all to do with chromosomes. They say that all foetuses in the early stages of development are female and it is only when a subtle chemical reaction happens in the womb that 49 per cent of those foetuses turn into males. The nipples are a throwback to those early days when, in fact, you were a girl.

Straight men get very worried about their nipples. They feel they have been emasculated if it is known that they get pleasure from them. Nipples are "women's stuff" and a lot of heterosexual males simply don't like having them touched. More fool them. The problem is that some men's nipples are more sensitive than others, so a lack of interest isn't always a result of hang-ups.

However, a friend of mine who has particularly receptive nipples says that he is convinced that there is a nerve which runs directly between the nipples and the end of his dick. If anyone plays with his tits he says he can feel it on his knob-end. So, gay men tend to make full use of the nipples in love-play. Tits respond well to licking, tweaking, rubbing, sucking, tickling and nibbling. Some men like to rub their cock on their partner's tits, bringing immense pleasure to an appreciative audience. Nipples have erectile tissue within their structure, and many men are very proud to display their tits when they are standing up in a little peak. Tit erections can be stimulated by sexual excitement or cold.

If you're biting the tits be careful not to break the skin as the nipples are sensitive and are prone to infection. If you are piercing the nipples in order to put rings through (and then hang weights from them), ensure that it's not heavy enough to tear the flesh.

Tit clamps, too, are popular with the S&M crowd. Ensure that they aren't too tight and don't stay on for too long. Those who like that sort of thing often improvise with the kind of clothes peg that has a spring in it.

Nocturnal Emission

This is the posh name for wet dreams – a phenomenon which most of us have experienced, particularly in youth. If we're feeling frustrated and badly in need of a bit of how's-your-father, our subconscious might try to help relieve the frustration by conjuring up very vivid sex dreams for us. Often these dreams are extremely filthy, and their startling realism tends to wake us up with a jolt and an intense orgasm. At which point we go "yuk!" as we realise our pyjamas are covered in spunk.

I personally never found nocturnal emissions much fun because they always left me feeling even more frustrated than when I realised it was all just a dream. Trying to go back to sleep to take up the dream where you left off never works.

The Kinsey Institute estimates that 80 per cent of men have experienced a nocturnal emission at some point in their life, but 100 per cent have experienced sexy dreams. Just think – James Anderton and John Major and Cliff Richard all have dirty dreams. Makes you go all nauseous, doesn't it?

Nocturnal Erections

It's not unusual for men to wake up with a steaming great hard on. At one time it was thought that this was because of the pressure of a full bladder, but in fact it now turns out that it is simply the last of around five erections that happen during sleep – mostly during the Rapid Eye Movement period. If you wake up prematurely, during REM, you'll more than likely have a boner on.

It is thought that these stiffies are nothing to do with the desire for sex but simply a combination of physiological and chemical reactions in the body. Erections require a combination of events in the brain, nervous system, blood system, muscles and body chemicals. Measurement during sleep show bursts of brain activity during the REM periods. These are accompanied by increased breathing rates and changes in the skin's electrical resistance. All these things point to an arousal of the nervous system.

Morning erections are seen by scientists as a sign of a man's general health and well-being. Men who are ill or under enormous stress have a greatly reduced amount of erection time during sleep.

It's also known that the level of the male hormone, testosterone, is at its highest first thing in the morning, which might also go some way to explaining the strength of erections we feel at that time of day.

Some research has been done into the frequency of morning erections at various ages and the results were:

- Age 20: 6 mornings per month
- Age 30: 7 mornings per month
- Age 50: 5 mornings per month
- Age 70: 2 mornings per month

No Hands

This is a novelty worth trying. You and your partner strip off (or not, as the fancy takes you) and then tie each other's hands behind your backs. This isn't an easy manoeuvre, but it can be done with a bit of perseverance. With your hands thus out of action, you attempt to have sex. This involves much heaving and straining, huffing and puffing, a lot of careful positioning and a great deal of frantic rubbing. It's amazing what you can do, and it's astonishing what other parts of your body you have to bring into play in order to achieve your ends.

Noises

We know that sight, touch and smell can provide erotic stimulation, but hearing is often neglected. Aural sex can come from all kinds of sources, whether it is dirty talk, heavy breathing, noisy bedsprings, creaking car suspension (when parked in a dark, secluded place), the crack of a whip or the smack of an arse, or that general squelching noise that we associate with the best kinds of sex. Usually there is some kind of lubrication involved, and when the motion begins, the lubricants provide a most sensual sound to accompany the general euphoria. Many people are connoisseurs of the noise emissions associated with orgasm. Some like to let rip with the kind of shouting and groaning that has the neighbours sending for the police, while others prefer the quieter type of orgasm, letting out a sort of melodic "ahhhhh!" followed by a long exhalation on the word "oh!" and then a physical collapse. For many men the noises made at orgasm could very well be used on the sound tracks of horror films, resembling as they do the moans of souls in torment. Agony and ecstasy – such close relations.

In the film "Frankie and Johnny", the character played by Al Pacino has recently been released from jail. His first sexual experience upon his release is conducted in total silence. The woman he is consorting with is unused to this kind of verbal restraint, and is slightly bewildered by the lack of sound. Unsure whether he has shot his load or not, she has to enquire of Mr Pacino if his thrustings have had a result. "Oh sure," he says, but then goes on to explain that after years in jail, with its lack of privacy, he has learned to come in silence. It is a habit he is finding hard to break. When, later in the picture, he finds the woman of his dreams, she manages at last to coax out of him an exultant roar of pleasure at the appropriate moment – an indication that he can truly claim to have become a free man.

A lot of men have mastered the art of ejaculating in total silence, stemming from their time living at home with parents. In some homes the walls are so thin that even heavy breathing would result in the institution of enquiries from other members of the family. Once out of earshot, however, most men like to make some kind of sound when coming.

The sound of water to accompany their sexual writhings is pleasing to some people, which accounts (in part) for the popularity of water beds, baths and showers. The glug, glug, splash, splash of the water becomes an integral part of the experience. Others spend a great deal of time searching out brass bedsteads with unoiled springs that will give maximum musical accompaniment to their erotic efforts. It all depends on how much privacy you need. If you are sharing the house with other people, they might not appreciate a nightly clanging, pinging, shouting and yelping as they drink their cocoa.

Most of us have tried, at some time, to have illicit sex in our parents' house. At times like that it is very important that there should be no noise whatsoever. They just think your friend Jimmy is staying over for the night for the sake of convenience and have no idea that you plan to spend those eight hours shagging each other rotten in the next bedroom to theirs. But how to manage this night of unbridled (but be-condomed) shagging without setting the alarm bells ringing? Well, to start with, you'll have to get out of bed. A little bit of bed-rocking can be explained by your having had a restless night, but a rhythmic pounding of the bed-head against the connecting wall might raise suspicions.

So long as the floor doesn't have creaky boards, you can get the duvet off the bed and pound away quite happily on the other side of the room from the wall through which sounds might be detected. Both of you must take a vow of silence. One small cry might be permissible ("Why did I shout 'Oh God! oh Jesus! oh Christ!' during the night, mum? I must have been having an ecstatic religious dream".)

If there is a lock on the door, make sure you use it; if not, jam a chair under the handle. Mums are experts at popping in to make sure you're both comfortable and asking whether you want a cuppa before she turns in. You certainly don't want her peeking round the door to find you and your friend...well...nude 'wrestling', perhaps?

Other noises associated with sex are sometimes embarrassing and unwelcome. Farting, for instance, can lead to blushes if it occurs during a passionate session with someone you're trying to impress. If you've had anal sex, there is often a farting noise as your partner withdraws. This is because his thrusts will have pumped some air into your anus, and it just gets expelled at the appropriate moment. Or it could just be that you've had baked beans on toast for tea.

Stomach gurglings, gagging (through deep throat sucking), coughing (through swallowing those pesky pubic hairs), spitting ("I told you to pull out before you came!") are all sounds familiar to the sexually experienced. All of them are natural, and each delicious in its own way.

Nonoxyl-9

This is a chemical present in some spermicides. The substance has been shown in laboratory tests to kill HIV. Some condoms are treated with Nonoxyl-9 as an extra precaution.

However, gay men should be careful about using such spermicides during fucking as they can irritate the inside of anus and cause nasty reactions in some people.

Non-reactive phase

This is the time, immediately after orgasm, when the erection goes down and no amount of stimulation will bring it up again. Also called the Refractory Period (q.v.). In young men this phase lasts between 15 and 30 minutes. It increases as we get older.

Numbers

Exactly what proportion of the populations is gay? This is an important consideration when working out the chances of finding your perfect soul-mate. Obviously the fewer gay men there are, the higher the odds against your finding just the right one for you (assuming that you are interested in only one). Well, there is some dispute over numbers, and it seems that we will never really know. In 1953 Alfred Kinsey published a report in the United States, based on five years research and a total of almost 8,000 interviews, suggesting that one in ten men were practising homosexuals. In 1988, however, a study carried out for the Health Education Authority estimated that 4 per cent of Britons were homosexual. In 1989 the US Committee on Aids Research found that 20 per cent of men had had some gay experience, while 3.3 per cent had homosexual sex "fairly often". In 1992 the science journal Nature reported that 6.1 per cent of British males had at some time had a homosexual experience. A similar survey in France found that one in four men had had sexual relations with another man.

A 1993 study conducted by the Seattle-based Battelle Human Affairs Research Centre found that only 1 per cent of men between 20 and 39 were exclusively homosexual, while 2.3 per cent had been sexually active with another man during the preceding ten years.

A Harris poll in April 1993 concluded that 4.4 per cent of men in the US had been involved in homosexual sex in the previous five years. In 1994 The National Survey of Sexual Attitudes and Lifestyles, sponsored by the Wellcome Trust, announced that only 1.1 per cent of men in Britain are gay.

Moralists are very pleased with these figures and conclude that because there are so few of us, there is little point in taking any notice if anything we say. However, when it suits their arguments, they still maintain that we are "very promiscuous" and trot out figures that suggest that gay men have on average 500 partners a year, and nonsense of that kind. Good grief, they can't have it both ways. If there are only handful of us in the country, where do we find 500 partners each?

All these figures have to be taken with a pinch of salt. Or, as writer A. N. Wilson commented on hearing this statistic: "If this is true, I must know every homosexual in the country and a few heterosexuals who, for their own perverse reasons, are posing as gay".

There are, of course, certain areas that have been colonised by homosexuals and turned into gay ghettos. Perhaps the most famous of these is the Castro area of San Francisco. Greenwich Village in New York and the Kings Cross area of Sydney, Australia also have high concentrations, and there is a 'gay village' in Manchester, England. In London, the Earl's Court area has always had a dense population of gay residents and now parts of Soho (particularly Old Compton Street) have been taken over and 'gayed.' Perhaps the biggest single gathering of gay men in Britain takes place each June in London at the Gay Pride Festival. Somewhere in that vast crowd of tens of thousands of homosexuals, there must be a man for you.

These are the areas to seek out if you want to stack the odds in your favour.

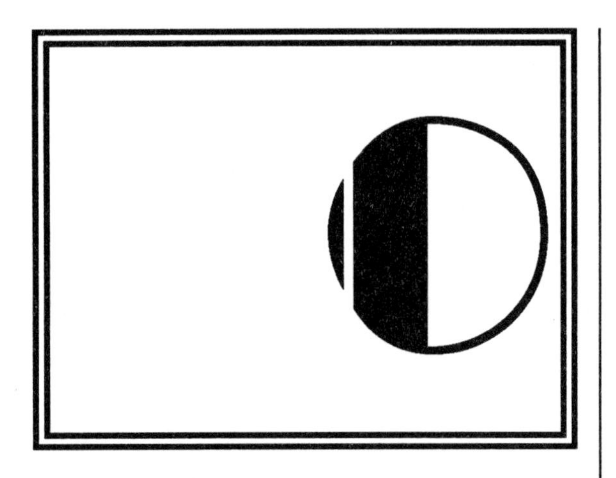

Olfactory Eroticism

The sense of smell has an important part to play in sexuality. The production of pheromones by the female can alert males to her sexual availability. Anybody who has a pet bitch in heat will testify to this after seeing the alarming effect it has on male dogs.

There are cells situated in the nose which are specially designed to detect the subtle aroma of pheromones; some species of moth can attract mates from many miles distant using this technique. The loss of the sense of smell, therefore, can have a devastating effect on some people's libido.

The word pheromone derives from two Greek words 'to carry' and 'to stir up'. All living things emit pheromones – and the human body secretes them in over three million glands. Research is being conducted into smells by Professor George Dodd, at the Warwick University's Institute of Olfactory Research. The good professor is convinced that smell is an essential ingredient in attracting a partner. As the relationship deepens, the subliminal scent of pheromones help the lovers feel comfortable with each other.

But what of gay men? Why doesn't the female pheromone trick work on us? Even if a woman were standing three feet away and had produced a bucket load of pheromones, I'm afraid I would fail to become excited. So is there a similar thing happening that makes me look at some men and think "woof, woof"? Is my hooter picking up their sexual smells and telling me to react? Or are there other factors at work telling me why I want to jump on some men (or have them jump on me) while others leave me indifferent?

I don't know, and perhaps it would be a reasonable avenue of scientific enquiry for Professor Dodd. If it turned out that gay men were, in fact, reacting to male pheromones rather than female ones, then we could all buy after-shave flavoured with the necessary chemicals and have every homosexual man in the street running after us with their tongues hanging out. Dream on, boys.

Olfactory erotophiles can, of course, be excited by other smells which have become associated in their minds with sexual experiences. Semen, with its pungent whiff of chlorine, is an obvious contender, but it could equally well be garlic (maybe he once had gorgeous sex with a Frenchman after eating *escargots Bourgignons*), or it might be sweat (associated with, perhaps, an experience in the locker room after a game). The aroma of urine might trigger sexy feelings in those who enjoy cottaging. Professor Dodd says that a particular variety of truffle virtually mimics testosterone's chemical make-up.

In French, the term for people turned on by smells is *renifleur* – from the verb *renifler*, to sniff.

Onanism has become another word for wanking, this time derived from the Bible (Genesis 38:9). In fact the Bible story concerns a man, Onan, who pulls out of his wife at orgasm and "spills the seed" that way rather than through a hand job.

Needless to say the Bible doesn't approve of jacking off, but then again, I don't approve of the Bible, so we'll leave it at that.

We should mention, however, that Dorothy Parker named her budgerigar Onan – because he kept spilling his seed.

On location

Not all sexual encounters need take place in bed, and in the gay world many of them take place in a variety of interesting locations. Cottages are one such, and very popular. But there are limitations. In even the most remote public lavatory there are likely to be unwelcome straight visitors – some in blue uniforms – who might interrupt the flow of activity. The extra *frisson* which cottages provide for some people is more than counteracted by the constant interruptions.

Some like to go on location to the beach, while others are fond of woodland settings and many find hotel rooms to have an aphrodisiac effect. The back of a car also comes high up on the list of favourites. I have known of people having sex in the broom cupboard of an hotel (as a change from the safety of the room). I knew one couple who liked to do it by an open window. One partner would lean out to talk to passing neighbours, while his friend down below and out of sight, would attend to his every whim orally. My friend got some kind of thrill from chatting amiably to people who would be horrified if they knew what was going on just out of sight.

One location which seems to be much prized is an aeroplane. Joining the six mile-high club is an ambition of many. It isn't easy, though. There is inevitably a queue for the lavs on 'planes and so it is difficult for two of you to unobtrusively enter and remain there for a few ecstatic minutes with the door locked. If you try it and some miserable nosy-parker spots what's going on, they will invariably send for the steward. But that's all right, he'll probably want to join you!

Whether you've decided to try having it away on the kitchen table or on the stairs, up against a tree or under water in the swimming pool, you'll find that new locations certainly add spice to sex.

OPPORTUNISM

Sexual opportunism is an overwhelmingly male characteristic. Let's face it, there aren't many women who go cottaging or cruising the Heath. Men, on the other hand, are much more quickly aroused, and some of them are ready for sex at almost any moment of the night or day (sorry all you outraged dykes, but it's a clinically observed phenomenon). I'm sure straight men would love to be able to have an equivalent to cottaging where they could go for a quick fuck for free and without any preamble or further obligation. But, whether it is cultural conditioning or natural reserve, most women don't operate like that. Even the ones who like a lot of sex would be unlikely to simply offer their genitals for five minutes of fun in a public lavatory.

But take women out of the picture, and you have two men who simply want to get their rocks off. There's no need for even the most elementary social niceties – they just whip their knobs out, do what they have to do, and go on their way; no need for conversation, drinks, flirting, persuasion or expensive meals in restaurants. If they were offered immediate sexual gratification with an attractive stranger, no questions asked, most men would be sorely tempted to take advantage.

In the male gay community, sexual opportunism is a way of life. No-one tuts and disapproves of liaisons which are undertaken between strangers with no other object than immediate sexual pleasure. In fact, it's almost expected. Of course, much of the gay world is geared up to create such 'opportunities'. Cruising and bar-hopping are both undertaken in the hope of an enchanted few moments of genital process (as the Archbishop of Canterbury persists in calling it) between gentlemen of like mind.

Sometimes the opportunity for sex comes along at times when we least expect it. The hunky married man who lives next door, and who you think is wasted on that wife of his, might suddenly invite you in for a drink one weekend when she is away. Or you could one day lock eyes with a business colleague across the boardroom table and become aware that further negotiations will be necessary outside of business hours. Sometimes you are just walking down the street when you get the impression that the youthful number passing by in his disgustingly ripped jeans is trying to attract your attention.

Oh yes, it can happen anywhere, anytime. In the cinema (popular because of the darkness), in the library, art gallery or on the bus. You'll discover that opportunity is knocking all over the place – so keep your antenna up in order to receive the incoming signals.

ORAL SEX

The lips, tongue and other parts of the mouth are extremely sensitive and are much employed in the enjoyment of sex. From kissing to fellatio, from nipple-nibbling to rimming, the use of the mouth is most important. Think of the useful and pleasurable sensations you can give and get from the gob – from the gentle licking and flicking of the tongue to the strong sucking mechanism. The movement of the lips, the lubricating qualities of saliva and the sheer warmth of this welcoming orifice. Without the mouth, of course, you wouldn't be able to talk dirty, either. Yes, oral sex (see Blow Job, Rimming, Kissing and Nibbling) is a major component of any gay man's repertoire.

ORAL SHIELD

For further information about this handy little addition to the safer sex armoury, see under Dental Dam.

ORGASM

Sexual arousal which leads to orgasm is a complicated business. It starts in the head with what is called *an appetite* – which is to say you have to be in the mood for sex. You have to have sexual thoughts, be feeling hot and randy and ready. Then, when all mental systems are go, the nervous system sends out messages to certain centres of the brain, causing measurable changes in the body. The blood pressure rises, heartbeat and breathing rates change, the penis begins to inflate, the muscles become more tense and the skin becomes more sensitive – at which point the sexual arousal intensifies and the whole process becomes self-perpetuating.

In men, the penis becomes erect and the testicles draw up closer to the body, after which the so-called *plateau stage* occurs. Arousal gets stronger, blood pressure rises further, breathing becomes more rapid, the heart beats faster and a "sex flush" that looks something like a rash can sometimes appear on the skin covering the chest, neck, or other areas of the body. There might also be an increase in the size of the testicles and head of the penis – which might also become darker in colour. A clear fluid (pre-cum) might appear at the tip of the penis. Other parts of the body become engorged with blood, too – the nipples, earlobes and lips, for instance, making them more sensitive.

If nothing distracting happens – like the phone ringing or someone disturbing you – and both partners feel secure enough to let go, then orgasm can occur. Orgasm lasts from three to 12 seconds (whereas the preceding stages might have lasted minutes or even hours). In men, orgasm includes two separate and distinct events, even though they seem to happen at the same time. The first is that the prostate gland, and other internal sex glands, force their fluids into the base of the urethra. Once this has happened, the ejaculation cannot be stopped. A few seconds later, the penis and the urethra contract, spurting the semen out through the tip of the penis. The anal sphincter also contracts at this point, and if you have ever had your fingers or cock in someone's arse when they are coming, you will have felt this effect quite distinctly.

As the mind focuses on these supremely pleasurable sensations, some people experience a sort of mini black-out. Brain-wave patterns change, and there will be involuntary noises and facial expressions as well as muscular contractions in the legs, buttocks and back.

The intensity of orgasm differs from one person to another, and it isn't the same every time. Muscle contractions can vary between a slight throbbing in the cock to wild thrashing as though a fit were occurring.

When the orgasm has finished, the body returns to its previous state. Blood flows out of the penis and it deflates. Sometimes it becomes flaccid almost immediately, while at other times it remains relatively firm for a few minutes afterwards.

The "quality" of an orgasm depends entirely on how it is perceived. Even a low intensity "coming" can be highly satisfying if it has been accompanied by generous amounts of foreplay and other pre-ejaculatory stimuli. Attempting to intensify orgasm by artificial means (such as inserting vibrators into the anus or sniffing poppers) can sometimes work, but if too much store is set on "how good" the orgasm was rather than on the success of the sexual encounter as a whole, then much of the pleasure and spontaneity can be lost.

Kinsey showed a relatively consistent frequency of orgasm in men. Between the ages of 15 to 25 it averaged 2 to 3 a week. Then there was a sudden upward peak at around age 30, followed by a steady decline with advancing age. Occasional orgasms were reported by men in the seventies and eighties. The word "climax" comes from the Greek word for ladder, and indicates the highest point or culmination.

There is a condition called Orgasmic Cephalagia, when orgasm causes a sudden blinding headache. It can be so painful that some people become reluctant to have sex because of it. Its origins aren't known, but some researchers think it might be connected with the changes in blood pressure. The condition usually clears up spontaneously.

ORGY

"Home is heaven and orgies are vile but you need an orgy once in a while" – Ogden Nash.

Orgies are of ancient Greek origin – later taken up by the Romans – and in those days involved wild dancing and singing, drinking, over-eating, cross-dressing, group sex and sometimes murder. Believe it or not, orgies started out as religious observances – the word actually means 'secret worship'. I think they ought to be restored to their rightful place in our spiritual life – it would certainly increase the number of people attending church on Sunday. Perhaps someone should raise the matter at the General Synod. Mind you, on reflection, the idea of having a daisy chain with the Pope and the Archbishop of Canterbury might not be such an appealing idea.

Nowadays, we cut the religious crap and use orgies as a good excuse to have it off with a number of people in one session. If you're planning an orgy there are certain things to remember. The first is that the gay variety is entirely illegal in Britain, so the information here is entirely for those who live in more civilised nations that don't have the arrogance to interfere in their citizens' private, consenting behaviour.

Keep the room warm and ensure that towels, tissues, toys, lubricants and condoms are available in abundance.

Subdue the lighting and be very careful about any background music you choose – constantly changing rhythms can be most distracting, so go for heavy rock with an insistent, sexy beat, or else something so very bland that you cease to hear it after a few minutes. Record a very long tape so that the music doesn't stop after forty-five minutes, plunging the room into a sudden, atmosphere-destroying silence.

Put on a mucky video and provide sufficient booze to get inhibitions down. Keep conversation to a minimum, perhaps having a 'time out' room where people can go to rest and converse between bouts. Encourage everyone to practise safer sex by liberally scattering condoms around the place and hanging lots of notices with the message: "This is a safer sex household". You might want to lay sheets or tarpaulins over your carpets to prevent crusting.

Giving your orgy a theme might help get things off the ground. Roman togas are always good, because they can be made very revealing, and so can centurions' gear. Swimwear is popular, as is fetish-wear and underclothing. If it's going to be a specialist party (such as S&M) choose your participants carefully, so that no-one objects.

For orgies that are slow to get off the ground, perhaps one of the more extrovert members of the group could put on a strip show with audience participation. Or, depending on your budget, you might be able to hire a professional or two.

Mixing and matching is sometimes difficult. We all like to imagine that if we went to an orgy it would be populated by gorgeous men who would make a bee-line for us as soon as we walked through the door. In reality there are likely to be people there who we don't fancy and who might have to be fended off. We might also have to cope with rejection ourselves. So, you need to be fairly confident and sexually secure (as well as experienced) to make the most of an orgy.

Inviting established couples is sometimes OK, and sometimes it leads to nasty incidents when submerged jealousies erupt. It all depends on the kind of relationship they have with each other.

Orgies can be fun, but they can also be disastrous as social events – it's amazing how many friends you can lose as a result of group sex. So, if you if you're hot to try an orgy, wangle an invite to someone else's – let them take the risks!

See also Group sex

P & P

This is a term used by the makers of pornographic films to indicate "pimples and penetration". It describes an extreme close-up shot of penetration, which also reveals any pimples or blemishes which the actor might have in that area.

Peg house

Peg houses could be found in some parts of south-east Asia. They were basically gay brothels where, between clients, the prostitutes sat upon wooden pegs to keep their anuses suitably dilated.

Penis

Cock, prick, dick, ding-a-ling, meat, blacksnake, pecker, willie, tool, wee-wee, tummy banana, one-eyed trouser snake (the last two coined by Australian humorist Barry Humphries), Jack, John, Peter, bayonet, beef, chopper, club, dagger, dang, dong, doodle, dork, dummy, hammer, hog, horn, hose, John Thomas, joy stick, love-muscle, middle-leg, pee-pee, poker, pole, prong, prodder, ramrod, root, sausage, tadger, thingy, wang, weenie, wiener, willy, and a thousand other words describe the penis – a man's primary piece of sexual equipment. Aristophenes, the Greek playwright had a veritable thesaurus of terms for it: eel, dried fig, acorn, punt, pole, twig and soup ladle.

The penis (a Latin word meaning 'tail') is a complicated organ, consisting of three spongy cylinders surrounding the urethral tube (down which the piss and cum travel). During sexual excitement – and at some other, less convenient, times – the spongy tissue becomes engorged with blood and makes the penis become stiff and erect. Powerful muscles at the base of the cock prevent a reverse flow of blood and help maintain the erection for as long as necessary.

The head, or glans, of the penis is covered in most instances by the foreskin, or prepuce. In some men this is very long, and in others quite short. Both variations are perfectly normal. The loose skin can be easily pulled back and forth over the head of the penis when it is in a relaxed state.

Penises have been subject to much discussion as to their aesthetic merits. Is a prick a thing of beauty or is it ugly, on a par with half a pound of tripe? I suppose it's all a matter of personal preference. Most of us consider our own little darling as the most gorgeous thing that ever hung between a man's legs (although we'd prefer him to be a little bit bigger), but when we look at other people's peckers, we have mixed reactions. Some, when erect and throbbing, are magnificent and a heart-stopping sight to behold, while others might be seen as repulsive, great knots of veins and ridges and purple engorgement.

Some are silky smooth to the touch, others are rough and knobbly. Some are huge and monstrous (two-handers as they're called in the trade) while others are petit, but complete in every detail.

Size queens love big dicks and pride themselves on being able to sense the presence of a monster at fifty yards, through six-inch steel sheeting. Indeed there is, within the gay community, a real mania about size. How many of our advertising images feature ridiculously bulging jock-straps or jeans with big baskets? And why else would we find Tom of Finland's deformed creatures so fascinating?

Manufacturers of sex aids are aware of this obsession and constantly entreat us to buy their latest gimmick for enlarging our pricks. You might have seen the so-called 'vacuum enlarger', into which the unsatisfactory pecker in inserted and then given an artificial blow-job with the help of a hand pump. It might be pleasant to use, but it won't make your cock any bigger. Then there's the special cream which is 'guaranteed' to enlarge the organ if you use it regularly – and only £15 a tube. The only problem is, *it doesn't work.*

But still the search goes on for the miracle that will turn a tiddler into a Titan. Miami urologist Harold M. Reed is promising the addition of inches in a $2,000 operation called augmentation phalloplasty, a procedure frowned on by British surgeons. Length is increased by up to one and three quarter inches by the snipping of a suspensory ligament at the top base of the penis.

A small London clinic is offering to inject fat taken from other parts of the body into the penis to widen the shaft. Men are queuing up for the operation, which works like this: first the patient is placed under a light general anaesthetic known as 'twilight anaesthesia'; which reduces side-effects and speeds recovery. Then fat is drawn from a selected part of the body using a large syringe. After a purification process it is injected into the shaft of the penis. It requires two small incisions, needing just a couple of stitches to sew up. The whole procedure takes under an hour. He is checked after a few days and then three weeks after surgery. If all is well, he is given the go-ahead for sex.

Respected surgeons are doubtful about the lasting effects of this operation and, at

£2,000 a go, it hardly seems worth the risk. One doctor who has seen the results of these operations says "Some of the fat cells sometimes don't take root and the result can look quite lumpy. The two penises I have seen after similar operations didn't look all that good." However, he goes on to say: "No matter how much you tell men that good sex is not just a matter of cut and thrust, they don't want to hear it. They believe size is everything. If that's what they want to think, and they've got £2,000 to spend, and it gives their ego a boost, then no harm done."

I'm not sure Mr Claudio Reyes, an American night-club singer, would agree. He died following an operation in which stomach fat was injected into his penis. It was probably the anaesthetic that killed him, but it just goes to show that surgery is a risky business, not to be undertaken lightly.

Be warned, what you see is what you've got – and whatever size it might be, it's unlikely to be 'too small'. If, however, you think you suffer from a condition called micro-penis, your doctor can refer you to a urologist, who can advise any course of action he thinks appropriate. This is a very rare condition indeed.

In America, researchers measured the flaccid (that is to say, non-erect) penises of 7,239 men. The largest in their survey was five and a half inches from the root, the smallest two and a quarter inches – the average was just under four inches. But the average erect phallus was around six inches. The researchers found that the smaller penises were capable of greater expansion – so if you see a pair of jeans bulging at the crotch, don't run away with the idea that you're going to get much more than that after the action commences.

What I want to know is: did the researchers get to play with all 7,239 pricks in the survey in order to get them to stand up for the second measuring? If so, I'm applying for a job with their research project immediately.

I know I'm probably pissing in the wind as far as size queens are concerned, but I have to repeat the oldest adage of all: It's not what you've got, it's how you use it that counts!

In the Hindu sex manual *The Karma Sutra*, there are three classifications of cock (which in those days was called the lingum). The hare (up to 5 inches long fully erect); the bull (up to seven inches) and the horse (up to ten inches.)

PENILE FRACTURE

You can't actually fracture the penis because there are no bones, but you can "snap it" although this is a very rare occurrence. One man reported how he was having a shag with his partner on top. His cock came out, but his partner didn't realise and sat down on it very hard. There was a snapping sound, and the penis bent to the left. He went straight to hospital, but when he arrived there he found his penis had gone black and so had his balls – this was because of the blood spilling from the ruptured member.

The penis is supported by a hydraulic system consisting of tubes, surrounded by tough tissue. When a penis is 'fractured', that tissue is ruptured. The most common way of getting to the split is by rolling down the foreskin, stitching up the injury with dissolving stitches, then rolling the foreskin back. Sometimes it results in a 'deviation', where the penis leans to one side. But usually the treatment effects a complete repair.

Penile frostbite

A joke? Not at all. According to *The British Medical Journal,* frostbite of the penis is one of the modern-day conditions which are being seen more and more by doctors. It occurs when joggers go out in sub-zero temperatures, wearing flimsy track suits and leave themselves open to this horrific occurrence.

The answer seems to be to get yourself a flannelette jock-strap.

Perversion

Perversion is another of those words which have been 'reclaimed' by the gay community (or maybe more accurately the queer community) and detoxified.

Now, instead of wilting at the mention of the word, young gay people revel in it. They describe their favourite social venues as 'pervy', which generally means that they are patronised by unapologetic fetishists, trannies, exhibitionists and sex freaks of all descriptions.

It surely must be healthier that people acknowledge and explore their consensual 'perversions', so please carry on doing so – and to hell with the *Daily Mail*.

Peyronie's disease

Named after a French surgeon of that name, Peyronie's disease describes the development of a severe curve in the penis which makes sex very difficult. Before jumping to the conclusion that you have this condition remember that many men have curves in their chopper, and it's perfectly natural.

There are three symptoms to Peyronie's: a curve that appears in adulthood in the erect penis; possible pain with erection; and a mass or hardened area on a section of the penis. This hardened area is caused by a build up of fibrous tissue.

There have been many treatments proffered over the years, but they are difficult to assess because Peyronie's disease sometimes clears up spontaneously with no treatment at all. How is a doctor to know whether his treatment is working or whether the condition would have disappeared anyway if left alone?

But a diagnosis is required by a specialist. Many men have perfectly normal curves in their penis and suffer no consequences throughout their lives. Peyronie's disease comes on relatively suddenly, so if you notice a dramatic change in the shape of your dick, then seek medical help.

Although Peyronie's is most usually seen in men between 40 and 60, it has been observed in men as young as 18.

PHENYLETHY-LAMINE

This is the chemical which our body produces when we're in love. It's the reason we feel so elated and excited when we think of, or are near, the man of our dreams. The same chemical is contained in chocolate, and so might explain that sweetmeat's reputation as an aphrodisiac. Why not take a leaf out of the Alice B. Toklas Cookbook (Ms Toklas was one of history's most famous lesbians) and try making some of her chocolate truffles?

Use the best chocolate you can find, with the highest available cocoa-solid percentage (Safeway's Continental Plain Chocolate is an incredible 74%).

Melt a quarter pound of chocolate in a microwave or in a dish over hot water (not over direct heat or it will go grainy), add 2 tbs butter and 2 tbs icing sugar. Stir until sugar is melted. Remove from boiling water, add 2 *very fresh* egg yolks, one at a time, stirring constantly. Add 2 tsp rum and mix thoroughly. Put away in cool place (not fridge) for 12 hours. Then shape into small balls and roll in powdered chocolate or cocoa. They are an exquisite little titbit to have before, after or during a lovemaking session.

PHIMOSIS/ PARAPHIMOSIS

Phimosis – or tight foreskin – is the condition whereby the opening of the foreskin is too small to let the head of the penis out, and so it doesn't draw all the way back. It can be painful for some people, and can also make it difficult to keep the penis clean. Don't try to force the foreskin over the penis if it won't go. You're liable not to be able to get it back again – and this might result in a medical emergency. This is called paraphimosis.

The condition can be corrected by circumcision (q.v.) if it becomes a nuisance or if sex becomes difficult or painful.

PIERCING

Piercing various parts of the body and adorning them with rings and other ornaments is nothing new. In ancient tribes, body piercing has become a major cultural statement. In some African nations, for instance, the holes that were pierced in the ear lobes were gradually made larger by the insertion of bigger and bigger plugs until, in some women, the lobes were stretched right down to their shoulders. Similarly, bottom lips were cut and plates of ever-larger proportions were inserted. This was considered beautiful to those involved.

Gay men have taken up piercing with a vengeance, and now you can see people walking around with rings in their nipples, their ears, their noses, their foreskins and even more intimate places. Piercing has become eroticised, and has been taken to great lengths by some men who are into it. At a recent Pride Festival I observed a man with no fewer than twenty gold rings in each ear lobe, as well as rings stuck through each titty and one through the nose. I don't know what agonies he endured for this decoration, but I'm sure he enjoyed it.

The most popular male genital piercing is called The Prince Albert, so called because it is rumoured that the Prince of that ilk had a ring through his penis in order to tie it to his leg, thereby avoiding "embarrassing situations". A hole is made through the glans of the penis into the urethra just above the frenum. A ring can then be worn that comes out of the penis and goes underneath.

Piercing the foreskin is also popular, placing a ring or barbell through so that the prepuce cannot be retracted. The *ampallang* is an horizontal hole through the glans and the *apadravya* is the vertical version. The *hafada* is a piercing through the scrotal sac, and a *guiche* piercing is through the ridge of flesh behind the scrotum, in front of the anal opening.

If you're thinking of having a few piercings, don't try and do it yourself – have it done by an experienced, trustworthy and hygienic professional, preferably one registered with the local Health Authority. Ensure that instruments are properly sterilised (i.e. in an autoclave, not just dunked in a bit of Dettol). The Director of Public Health says: "All needles should be bought in sterile and only used once, then disposed of in a 'sharps' bin." The pain can be deadened with the use of anaesthetic gels, although many devotees of piercing insist that the process is not painful when carried out by experts.

You should also remember that such piercing is legal if it is for decorative purposes alone. If there is any suggestion that you may be getting sexual pleasure from the piercing, then it could well be against the law. There has been a case (before the notorious Operation Spanner) when a body piercer was given a fifteen month suspended sentence when the judge decided he was piercing a client for the purposes of sexual pleasure. The whole area is now confused, so beware and be warned.

Don't be tempted to wear cheapo jewellery through your piercings, particularly if you are having rings or other metal objects inserted near the head of the penis – the metal can leech into the urethra causing horrific conditions if the metal reaches the kidneys or other organs.

A plastic surgeon says that he has never treated anyone who has been injured by body piercing and thinks that as long as it is done by an experienced practitioner, using clean instruments, it is probably safe. But he has doubts about the wisdom of piercing "sensitive" organs. "Some people scar badly," he said, "They develop keloids – large scarred areas – which are difficult to treat."

Remember to remove any adornments before going through airport metal detectors, or you might have some very embarrassing explanations to give.

- Patrick of London Body Piercing Clinic. Tel: 0181 656 7180 for an appointment.
- Wildcat International, Europe's largest supplier of body jewellery, accessories and associated paraphernalia. For free catalogue contact: Wildcat International, 16 Preston Street, Brighton BN1 2HN.

PLETHYSMOGRAPHY

A plethysmograph is a contraption which can be attached to an individual's penis in order to measure the extent of sexual arousal when the subject is exposed to various sexual stimuli. Even a very small change in the size of the dick can be detected by this device. It has been used in the past to try to ascertain people's sexual orientation by showing them photographs of both sexes and seeing which one registers the biggest reaction on the old plethysmograph.

It was first used by a Czech psychologist called Kurt Freund, who was trying to change people's sexual orientation. Needless to say, he wasn't trying to turn straight people gay. He found that the men who came to him to be "cured" and who underwent aversion therapy, didn't stay cured long.

He abandoned attempts to alter people's sexuality, but the plesthymograph remains a useful tool for finding out what a person's real sexual preferences are – whether they are prepared to admit them or not.

Although it has all the makings of a tool of oppression, it hasn't been used as such. Yet.

Pornography is as old as man, but the word itself is derived from the Greek (*porne* – prostitute; *graphen* – to write). Every culture that has ever existed has recorded the pleasures of sex in whatever medium was available to them. Anyone who has been on a conducted tour of the ruins of Pompeii will have been treated to a glimpse of the famous wall paintings. In ancient India the scholars of eroticism recorded their findings in guide books like The Kama Sutra and in temple sculptures. In Ancient

Greece, sexual scenes were depicted in graphic and slavering detail on vases – with plenty of gay-oriented scenes.

An excellent collection of erotica from down the ages has been assembled in Amsterdam's sex museum, and unlike the fuddy-duddy British Museum, it's open to anyone with the price of admission (which is very moderate). You can see mediaeval dildoes, 19th century engravings, clockwork cocks and mucky music boxes.

As the methods of recording and depicting sexual activity have become more and more sophisticated, so the market for pornography has grown. The invention of photography was the jumping off point, and within days of this new technology becoming available, the pioneer porn merchants were taking pickies of their wives with their bloomers round their ankles – or in the case of Lewis Carol, little girls, similar. You no longer had to imagine what other people did – you could buy photographs and see for yourself.

Some of the first homo-erotic photographs were taken under the guise of being for the use of artists who could not find live models. Usually they were of men in statuesque poses. These photographs were so widely distributed that it was obvious that not only artists were using them.

Among the first to treat male eroticism seriously in photography was a German living in Sicily, Wilhelm Baron von Gloeden (1856-1931). He got the local boys to abandon their clothes and pose in "classical" manner for his camera.

As the technical innovations made photography widely available, more gay men saw its potential. During the early part of the century, homoerotic pictures were generally of the "health and physical culture" type. The popularity of nudism in the 1920s and 30s also gave an excuse to legitimately capture naked men on film.

Real "hard-core" porn is, of course, illegal in this country. But that doesn't mean to say that you can't get it. It is the best form of sex education anyone could wish for. A good graphic depiction of sexual activity is far better than a dry instruction to "use your imagination". A video of the action is even better, because then you can see for precisely how to do the movements and everything. A picture, after all, speaks much more eloquently than words in this instance, especially when it is accompanied by a soundtrack of heavy breathing, dirty talking and uninhibited shouting during orgasm.

There are, though, some disadvantages to porn. Many videos still in circulation were made back in the seventies and early eighties when the porn-stars knew little or nothing about safer sex and, as a result, condoms are never seen. The latest films, though, often do feature condoms, but the new convention seems to be – don't show the rubber actually being put on. It only becomes apparent that johnnys are in use when the penetration has been effected. It would be a great service to our community if the makers of these films used their powerful influence on our sexual behaviour to eroticise condoms, making their application a much more integral part of the action.

There is little doubt that porn videos have changed the face of gay sex. They have introduced us to activities which many of us would never have thought of if left to our own devices. Rimming, for instance, was almost unheard of in the sixties; nowadays it is widely practised, and I'm convinced that is because it has been made desirable by the powerful imagery used in pornography.

Other conventions which porn videos generally observe: the orgasm must always occur in full view, consequently the actors always "pull out" at the crucial moment in order to shoot their load. In real life this isn't generally the case, although if you want to shoot while inside someone ensure that you are wearing a condom.

The actors (perhaps 'performers' would be a better word) almost invariably have large dicks, sometimes gigantic (perhaps most famous is that of Jeff Stryker). This can give the impression that everyone but the viewer is well hung, and can lead to feelings of inferiority. The truth, of course, is that the actors are generally chosen for these films because they are bigger than average. Low camera angles can also exaggerate the size. After all, the videos are there to provide fantasies, and most of us fantasise about size.

Indeed, many things in these films are not often quite as simple as they seem. Editing techniques can ensure that we get the impression that it is possible for some men to ejaculate several times in the space of ten minutes or so. This isn't true, of course – often the films are made over a period of several days and the orgasms edited together to appear as though they have all occurred in one session. Or the ejaculation is filmed from several different angles, and with clever splicing it can appear that the orgasm is lasting about three minutes.

It is not beyond the film-makers to use lightly beaten egg white to simulate semen, either. If the actor is having problems getting an erection, filming may be delayed for hours, but you'd never know it – it seems that porno actors have permanent and ever-ready hard-ons. Judicious editing and even special effects can create super-studs where none really exists. Each of the modern porn 'studios' has its own style and its own fans.

William Higgins took over from the early porn merchants like the Athletic Model Guild and Colt and refined the art – and was extremely prolific in output. The French films of J. D. Cadinot are very popular, featuring as they do many young models from all over Europe.

The soft-core videos that are legally available in Britain have mushroomed in number. They are generally a disappointment, promising all and delivering little.

Some people still prefer the written variety of porn, and dirty stories have lost none of their appeal. They do allow you to use a bit more of your imagination and, therefore, become more involved in the goings on. Much the same can be said about still photography. You can project your own fantasies on to those caught in a split second of ecstasy. It is difficult with videos because when the actors speak they sometimes come over as very unpleasant or pathetic individuals, or the erotic charge gained from seeing their rippling muscles and gigantic equipment is undermined when are accompanied by a high-pitched or whining voice.

- Fascinating fact: although pornographic films are termed 'blue movies' in the Western world, in the Philippines they're referred to as green.

- Wonderfully erotic male photographs can be obtained from Mike Arlen, Wetherby Studios, 23 Wetherby Mansions, Earls Court Square, London SW5 9BH. Ask about the latest edition of his cult magazine Mike Arlen's Guys.

POSTILLIONAGE

This is a French word meaning fingering the anus. See *fingering* for further particulars. It's peculiar how often things sound more romantic when rendered in French.

PRE-CUM

During sexual arousal, but before ejaculation, a fluid is produced the purpose of which is thought to be lubrication. It is commonly called pre-cum and men produce it in differing quantities at different times. Some men hardly produce any, others seem to be swimming in it.

Be aware that pre-cum does contain some semen which might be infected with HIV. Those who imagine that it is safe to have a penetrative fuck and pull out before ejaculation should realise that pre-cum can be just as dangerous as semen. The answer is to wear a condom from the beginning to the end of any penetrative sex.

PREPUCE

"Infamy! Infamy! They've all got it in for me!" This was the plaintive cry of Kenneth Williams in *Carry on Cleo* and, if it could only talk, the poor old foreskin might echo it. Through the ages people have been wanting to chop it off either for religious reasons (God loves you more, it seems, if you've had your genitals mutilated), hygiene reasons (which are being questioned by some medical experts), or because people consider that they'll get more sexual pleasure without their prepuce (no evidence to prove this either way).

The British Medical Journal revealed the facts about the foreskin in a 1993 article. Before birth, as the foreskin develops, it is fixed to the head of the penis. At birth the foreskin can be pushed back over the head of the penis in only 4 per cent of boys. By the age of five this proportion has risen to 90 per cent and by the age of 17 it is close to 99 per cent.

If the foreskin does not retract after this age, then the condition is termed phimosis (see under that heading). There is little risk of cancer from retaining your foreskin – indeed, even though only 7 per cent of British males are circumcised the incidence of penile cancer is minute. Those cases that do occur seem to be related to smoking. Washing carefully under the foreskin to keep it clean will ensure that there are few medical problems. Inflammation of the penis is called balinitis (q.v.).

The debate on whether a cock looks more attractive with or without the foreskin rages endlessly in gay magazines. It comes down to personal choice and, I suspect, early experiences. If you are absolutely resolute in your preference for cut cock, then I suggest you emigrate to Israel where they have an Army which must rank among the best-looking, if most brutish, in the world, and is absolutely one hundred per cent shorn of foreskin.

However, those who have been circumcised when they were a child, and then want to be uncircumcised in later life, now have a champion. He is Dr Jim Bigelow, a Californian psychologist who resented having his foreskin removed as a child and wanted to "redevelop" it. He has developed a technique for stretching the foreskin so that it covers most of the head of the penis when it is flaccid. The treatment goes as follows:

Stage 1. The skin of the shaft is pulled forward over the head of the penis and then held in place by a strip of adhesive tape which runs from both sides of the penis over the glans (another, smaller piece of tape stuck the other way round prevents the tape adhering to the glans). A space is left for urination, of course. This is worn 24 hours a day. A two-ounce lead fishing weight can be attached to the middle of the tape to exert further pull.

Stage 2. Once enough new skin has developed for it to be stretched over and beyond the glans, a strip of tape seven-eighths of an inch long is wrapped around the tip of the skin to form a ring. The weight is attached again.

Stage 3. Devices are used to allow for further skin expansion. A foam rubber cone is fitted over the glans to give extra length, and the foreskin is taped over it.

Further reading:

- *The Joy of Uncircumcising*, published by Hourglass Book Publishing. Details from Dr. Jim Bigelow, Uncirc, PO Box 52138, Pacific Grove, California, USA 93950.

PRIAPISM

This unfortunate condition arises when an erection simply refuses to go down. The penis stays stiff despite the fact that there are no sexual feelings or desires and no stimulation. The erection can remain hard for days or even weeks with no sign of deflating and is, of course, most inconvenient and painful.

Until recently it was thought that priapism was caused by failure of the nerves which control the muscles at the base of the penis. These muscles are responsible for allowing the blood which inflates the penis to flow backwards and forwards when necessary. If they cease to function properly during an erection, they may simply not allow the erection to go down.

The latest research has found that a gas, nitric oxide, which is present in car exhaust fumes and cigarette smoke, is produced in the main nerve of the penis and causes the organ to expand when stimulated. Overproduction of nitric oxide could be responsible for priapism.

The researchers suggest that a cure might be found by blocking the body's production of nitric oxide. Conversely, administering extra nitric oxide might help with impotence.

At present priapism is treated either with injections or by draining some of the blood.

PROMISCUITY

A word so loaded that it can mean almost anything. How many partners does one have to have before one can be considered promiscuous? Fundamentalist Christians would tell you that if you have sex with anyone but your spouse, you are promiscuous. The charge that because they enjoy exploring their sexuality, gay men are 'promiscuous' is just another way of insulting us. Besides which, gays didn't invent promiscuity. Don Juan and Casanova were straight.

My favourite unapologetic promiscuous person was Mae West who is reported to have said – after being told that there were eleven men waiting outside her dressing room door – "I'm tired, send one of them away."

PROSTATE CANCER

The prostate is a small, chestnut-shaped organ which lies under the bladder and in front of the rectum. In most men it starts to increase in size after the age of fifty, under the influence of the hormone testosterone. A study found that in 45 per cent of over-50s the gland was significantly enlarged. About 70 per cent of 70-year-olds experience trouble. As the prostate gradually begins to compress and distort the urethra – the tube that runs the length of the penis and through which urine is discharged from the bladder. Men may experience difficulty in starting to urinate, and the stream is weak. Incontinence might result and there will be a frequent urge to urinate during the night.

An enlarged prostate is a real inconvenience, and even a danger.

One in ten men with an enlarged prostate will be suffering prostate cancer – the third largest killer of men in Britain – that's 9,000 deaths a year.

Regrettably, only 15 per cent of men suffering from prostate cancer are identified in time to cure the disease.

The reluctance to seek treatment often stems from embarrassment. The doctor can check you out with a DRE (a digital rectal examination – something many gay men do for fun!) or with a blood test.

There are several indicators that may increase your risk of developing prostate cancer:

- Hereditary: If a man's father or brother has had a prostate cancer, his risk rises by 2.8 times. If an uncle or grandfather has also been affected, the risk rises by six times.

- Radiation: exposure to nuclear radiation can double the chances of developing prostate cancer.

- Diet: Many studies suggest a link between prostate cancer and a high fat intake.

- Sex: the younger a man was when he had his first sexual intercourse and the more sexual partners he has had, the commoner the prostate cancer.

New treatments are being developed all the time. If the experiments with lasers now taking place in St. Bartholomew's hospital are successful, those requiring treatment may only need to be day patients. Drugs are also being developed which shrink the prostate and so relieve many of the symptoms. Traditional surgical treatments have left some men with a condition called Retarded Ejaculation, which is explained under that heading.

But if you are having trouble with your waterworks, take your courage in both hands and present it to the doctor. Remember that one in three men over fifty is affected by Benign Prostatic Hyperplasia, or non-cancerous swelling of the gland. Symptoms include difficulty in starting to urinate, weak stream, starting and stopping mid-stream, discomfort when urinating, dribbling, having to rush to the lavatory, more frequent urinating, having to get up several times at night to urinate, incontinence or a sudden inability to urinate. To check this condition the GP will examine the prostate gland by gently inserting a finger into the rectum. There may also be blood and urine tests and possibly a referral to a specialist. Treatment includes drugs such as anti-spasmodics to lower the pressure on the bladder Treatment will not necessarily affect your sexual functioning, but it might save your life.

Prostatitis

An infection or inflammation of the prostate gland and commonest between the ages of 25 and 45. It can be caused by bacteria or by taking exercise with a full bladder. Possible tests include genital and rectal examination, urine and blood tests and swabs from the end of the penis. There may also be referral to a specialist. If the cause is an infection, antibiotics will be prescribed. Sometimes natural food supplements, such as rye pollen extracts, may be used to reduce inflammation. Other drugs such as anti-spasmodics can be used to lower the pressure on the bladder or alpha blockers to relax the muscles.

Except in severe cases, surgery is rare.

Pubic hair

Pubic hair is classified as a secondary sexual characteristic and has a much coarser texture than head hair, as anyone who is fond of cock-sucking and has had a throat full of long, tough hairs will tell you. It frames and complements our dangly bits a treat and, of course, has become the focus of much attention down the ages. There are those who like to shave it off completely in order to give more emphasis to the genitals (although I always think you've got to have an extremely beautiful three piece suite to get away with this). Some, however, find the absence of pubic hair most disconcerting. There are those who topiarise their pubes into interesting shapes such as hearts or question marks.

I was once a nurse, and one of my jobs was to shave male patients in preparation for surgery. Of course, I was very professional and dispassionate at the time, but I must say my heart always gave a little flutter when I was called to do a shaving in the orthopaedic ward. It was there that the active young athletes who had injured themselves in sporting mishaps were situated. If they'd been in traction for some time, totally immobile, their juices would be running. And this is the source of many fantasies, which will be left to your imagination. Draw those curtains, nurse!

Pubic lice

In France they are called *papillons d'amour* or butterflies of love, in America they refer to them as crotch crickets, here we call them crabs.

This is one little sexual infestation that you *can* catch from a lavatory seat! Or from mucky bedding. Generally, though, the little bleeders are passed from one person to another through intimate bodily contact. I call them little bleeders because that's precisely what they are – tiny, crab-shaped insects that suck your blood and leave itchy, nasty sores where they've been feeding. The itching can be particularly bad at night.

Fortunately they aren't dangerous and are relatively easy to get rid of. But here's a warning: do not under any circumstances be tempted to spray yourself with domestic insecticides or fly-killers. They are not made for this purpose and can be very dangerous if they get into your body through your skin. Stick to the preparations you can buy over the counter from the chemist, following the instructions meticulously. Some crabs have become resistant to certain treatments, so you might have to try more than one brand.

Check other hairy parts of your body (under arms, eyebrows, eyelashes and hairy chests) to ensure that they aren't at home there, too. Shampoo the carpets in case little nits are lurking there. Your bed clothes and any garments you've been in contact with since the infestation should be washed at a high temperature, then you should be OK.

If you are absolutely horrified at the prospect of crabs lurking in your house, an extreme answer is to vacate the premises for a fortnight. The crabs will die within twenty-four hours if you aren't there to feed off, and the nits (eggs) which take a week or so to hatch, will also die within twenty-four hours of emerging when there isn't a human meal ticket around.

Preparations to ask for at the chemist:

- Carylderm, Quellada, Derbac M or Prioderm.

PVC

A plastic material sometimes used to make waterproof clothing. It has become a fetish material and a big turn-on for some. It is now possible to buy all kinds of garments made from shiny and clingy PVC. See Leather for the address of suppliers.

QUANTITY VERSUS QUALITY

Having dispensed with the meaningless term 'promiscuity', we now move on to comparisons. What matters about relationships is not the quantity but the quality. Was the encounter pleasurable? Did it make both participants feel good about themselves and each other? Was a good time had by all?

It's difficult to judge what constitutes a "successful" sexual encounter. Is it merely whether your partner gave you a particular thrill? That he went along with all your desires? That he was mind-bogglingly beautiful in face and body? That he was skilled in the ways of sexual excitement?

Or is it to do with how we feel about ourselves in the afterglow? Did the encounter polish up our self-esteem? Did we come away from it feeling that not only had we been satisfied but that we had come closer to another human being, that our innate separateness from each other had been dismantled, even if only momentarily?

Some of my best sexual encounters have not been the wild, violent and passionate ones, but the quiet, affection and loving ones. If you manage to include both features, then that's special.

A first-time sexual encounter with someone you don't know very well can be strained and embarrassing. It takes time to familiarise yourselves with each other's bodies. It often takes time to really get the sex right, and this is where continuing relationships often score over one-night stands. As you begin to feel more comfortable with each other, the sex often gets better, less fraught and more loving. (See also Disasters).

I offer no answer to questions about which is best, quantity or quality, but I do maintain that they rarely go together.

QUARTET

A foursome has a dynamic that is quite different to a threesome. Although four people having sex together might appear to have a lot of options going for them (actually, it seems fewer than a threesome) it is more than likely that they will split up into two couples after a while – or a threesome with someone left out.

Add one more person and you're into orgy territory, which is a different thing altogether. A foursome still has the possibility of providing moments of intimacy for all the participants at once.

QUEEN

Queens are the traditional manifestation of effeminate homosexuality. The word "queen" can be preceded by a number of adjectives to define it. A drag queen loves to dress up in frocks and wigs of extravagant design and will often present to the world an overblown persona to go with the clothing. Perhaps the most famous and best-loved drag queen of our generation is Lily Savage.

Snow queens are usually black gentlemen who prefer to take their sexual pleasure with white gentlemen. Drama queens can be of either sex and are epitomised by Bette Davis, Joan Crawford, Barbara Stanwyck and just about any man who enjoys emotional overstatement.

Size queens prefer to entertain gentlemen with sexual equipment of generous or even eye-watering proportions. The bigger the better, and for a size queen there is no such thing as 'too big'.

Brand queens are becoming more and more common within gay circles. These are the people who will only don clothing with specific designer labels, only eat food from specialist shops, drink champagne of a certain *grand marque* and so on. They are particularly concerned about which brand of jeans they wear, and even more so about the make of underwear they choose. Fashions come and go with alarming rapidity, and brand queens are fickle. I will, therefore, refrain from making any suggestions as to which brands are presently in vogue.

Closet queens are those who are gay but refuse to acknowledge the fact to other people or sometimes even to themselves. And poison queens have a razor-sharp line in put-downs, insults and evil comments.

A sandwich queen likes to be in the middle of a threesome, fucking and being fucked at the same time. A camp queen is a man with noticeably effeminate characteristics. Opera queens are often brand queens out on the town. They can be observed in the crush bar at Covent Garden or at the Coliseum. Dolled up in their Armani clothes, reeking of whatever after-shave is presently *de rigeur,* they will be complaining that only Möet et Chandon is available at the bar.

In days gone by, queens would communicate with each other in a secret language called "polari". This was most publicly illustrated in the outrageous sixties radio comedy series "Round the Horne". Polari was featured in the sketches involving camp queens Julian and Sandy (played by Kenneth Williams and Hugh Paddick). Here is a short glossary of polari in case anyone feels they'd like to revive its use: *palare* – talk; *bona* – good; *vada* – look; *omi* – man; *palone* – woman; *omipaloni* – homosexual; *riah* – hair; *lallies* – legs; *dolly* – nice; *eek* – face; *naph* – bad; *nante* – none/nothing; *lucoddy* – body; *fantabulosa* – excellent; *troll* – walk; *lattie* – house. And so theatrical queens of the fifties and sixties would greet each other with the expression: "Lovely to vada your dolly old eek." Naturally there were many words for particular sexual characteristics and activities so that queens could point out anything interesting to each other without scaring the horses.

When queens get together the noise level is likely to rise considerably. Because of this, the collective noun for queens is "a scream".

The gay community was rent asunder recently by the so-called reclaiming of the word "queer" from the hands of our oppressors. Radical activists advised us that "gay" was no longer the right word with which to define ourselves, it was too middle-class and exclusive. They told us that from now on we should refer to ourselves as queer, so that we could stand shoulder to shoulder with all other sexual minorities and thereby gain strength. Queer would be an inclusive word that would take in lesbians, bisexuals, sado-masochists, paedophiles – the lot. In reclaiming the word we would 'detoxify' it. Our enemies would be deprived of its use as a poisonous insult.

Not everyone was convinced. Homosexual women continue to call themselves lesbians and dykes, straight sado-masochists were unhappy being grouped with gays. The political intention of adopting Queer to bring people together has failed. People in sexual minorities want to know what particular kind of sexual minority they are in. Gay is more precise.

The concept of queer was explained by one of its proponents as: "A way of imagining futures, different possibilities. Queer culture is not political in the sense of projecting a positive image, the restrictive mainstay of lesbian and gay culture. Lesbian and gay art ended up talking itself into a corner, censoring itself. It looked at things the wrong way round – what they wanted to express got lost in how they wanted to express it. Queer culture, by contrast, is 'in your face'. It makes no apologies for itself, asks no favours and makes no attempt to fit into comfortable norms."

This spokesperson for queer culture says that the main expression has been in film. I have to say, though, that most of the 'queer cinema' I've seen has been just about unwatchable.

That said, queer does seem to have found its niche among the cognoscenti. If someone is calling themselves "queer", you can bet they live in London or Manchester's gay village and are planning the overthrow of the world and everyone in it.

Many less privileged homosexuals, particularly those in Cleckheaton, still shudder at the prospect of "queer" being applied to them.

QUEYRATERY-THROPLASIA

If you spot a red, velvety irritation around the end of your penis, it could be the above-mentioned condition (sorry, there isn't enough space to repeat it). It is rare, and usually occurs in older people. But it is pre-cancerous, and if you think you have it, see your doctor at once.

QUICKIE

Everyone knows the value of a quickie - known in America as a "bunny fuck". You just need to get your rocks off, with no preliminaries and no need for formalities afterwards. Between men this if often acceptable and understood. Of necessity cottagers can specialise in the quickie.

But the quickie can be useful to long-established couples too. Sometimes you wake up in the morning with a large-scale erection that simply demands to be seen to before you go to work. If the lover is laying there beside you, and you explain that you'd like to spill your seed, but have only got three minutes to achieve it, most men will be happy to oblige.

Randy

If we're feeling randy our body is telling us that we want to have sex. At times like this our thoughts might turn almost obsessively towards getting our end away. We might find our hands frequently reaching "down there", as though there was an itch (which indeed there is), and we might even start getting involuntary erections. Randy feelings occur when the prostate gland tells us that it has produced a large amount of seminal fluid and wishes to discharge some of it.

When we're randy and there is no immediate relief we might become restless and fidgety, pacing about until eventually we either go out and find a partner or have a wank to take the pressure off. Randy feelings are extremely pleasant when there is the prospect of them being satisfied, but frustrating when nothing can be done about them.

Rape

Non-consensual sex wasn't considered much of a problem in the gay community until recently, when Project Sigma, a group doing research into male homosexuality, discovered that a significant number of their subjects had been forced by other men to have sex against their will.

Now more men are prepared to come forward and admit that they've been raped. But there seem to be two kinds of male rape: the kind that is inflicted on gay men by other gay men, and the sort that happens in public places, where men are chosen at random – usually by a gang of heterosexuals – and forced to have sex.

The first type of rape happens between gay men who have, perhaps, initially agreed to have sex. One of them changes his mind, but the other won't take "no" for an answer. All the arguments that apply to straight "date rape" are applicable here. No-one has the right to invade someone else's body against their will, no matter what has gone before. It doesn't matter if you're naked in bed together, it should still be possible for one partner to say "I've changed my mind", without the prospect of being forced into sexual activity. The problem is that we often choose our partners because of their size and strength, and we can find ourselves powerless against such a person if things turn non-consensual.

The second sort of rape was in the news recently when a young man had been abducted from a train and claimed to have been raped by a gang of thugs.

It is often said that random rape in semi-public places is more about violence than sex, and psychologists have proposed that most of these attacks are, in fact, carried out by straight men as a means of humiliation. As Dr Gillian Mezey, a psychiatrist and co-author of *Male Victims of Sexual Assault* says: "Such attacks are carried out by heterosexuals as a perverse form of 'gay-bashing'. By raping someone they think is homosexual the attackers are able to express both their hatred of gays and their sexual aggression."

Just as other rapists seem to get some kind of pleasure from degrading and violating women, this pleasure seems to be increased if they can do it to a man.

Rape may figure in sexual fantasies, and be incorporated into the story line of some gay videos, but in reality it is a nasty and vicious thing.

Group to contact:

- Survivors, a telephone help line for the survivors of male rape. 0171-833 3737 (Tues, Wed, Thurs 7-10pm).

RATE OF INCREASE OF SEXUAL PLEASURE

Dr. Elizabeth Stanley proposed that sexual pleasure developed and increased in eight definable steps. She called this her "Ladder of Sexual Pleasure". At ground level there is no interest in physical contact for sexual pleasure. On the first rung of the ladder there is physical pleasure from non-genital contact e.g. cuddling – but little or no genital sensation. On Rung 2 there is stronger physical pleasure, but still no genital sensation. On Rung 3 moderate sexual arousal is experienced with partial erection. On the fourth rung there is strong sexual arousal with a full erection. On Rung 5 there is intense sexual arousal with feelings of discomfort if orgasm does not occur. The sixth rung is orgasm and, finally, on rung 7 there are the good feelings afterwards.

Ever smoked a cigarette at the top of a ladder?

REDUNDANT PREPUCE

This is the medical term for a long and copious foreskin. As we've already noted, foreskins come in all shapes and sizes, and some people have so much they can achieve something called "docking" (q.v.).

Reflexes

Bodily reflexes happen automatically, without our will and sometimes without our consent – as any young man whose had an unwanted erection at the swimming pool will testify.

One reflex with which we are all familiar is the monoclonic jerk. This has nothing to do with masturbation, but is that strange twitch that sometimes occurs just as we're going to sleep. When we're in bed with someone and they're just about to pass into the land of nod, it is as well to keep goolies well covered as a monoclonic jerk might cause the nackers to be kneed.

The cremasteric reflex is another interesting one you might have noticed. It's observable when the testicles seem to move around of their own volition inside the scrotum. It usually happens when we are touched on the inner thigh or when someone is stimulating one of our other erogenous zones. Nobody knows why our bollocks squirm like this when we're touched in sexually sensitive places.

Refractory Period

This is the time just after orgasm when the cock deflates and you lose interest for a while. No amount of stimulation will get you going again. The libido needs time to regenerate. Depending on the situation (it might be wild sex with a dreamboat you've just met or it might be routine stuff with your lover of ten years' standing) the refractory period might last half an hour or it might be three hours. And for older men it might be a matter of days before they feel they can do it again. However, some younger men find that in some instances, if stimulation continues even after they've ejaculated, they can become aroused again almost immediately.

There is also something called a paradoxical refractory period, a phenomenon observed in older men who may require 12 hours or more to attain another erection if foreplay has been interrupted and the erection lost before orgasm takes place.

Relationships

Gay relationships have had a bad press for a long time. "They don't last" is the commonly held view, but this is not universally true, and I know of gay men who have lived happily together for twenty-five years and more.

Having said that, it is quite an achievement to keep a gay partnership going over the long term. As well as the usual pressures of two people living together (having to adjust to each other's living pattern can be a great strain), there is the added pressure from outside. Unlike heterosexual relationships, which are expected and encouraged, the gay variety are generally frowned upon. Our parents and relatives are unlikely to give us an extravagant, wholehearted wedding ceremony to wish us well. On the contrary, they are likely to be disapproving of our living arrangements and might even try to actively undermine them.

As they develop, gay relationships change. At the beginning, everything revolves around sex and romance (see under that heading), but as time passes the focus changes to home-making and adjustment. Instead of being totally wrapped up in each other, we tend to start looking outwards again. Over the years, the sexual element is likely to wind down – we may still want sex, but less frequently with our partner. At this stage there might be "outside" sexual partners, and another pressure – jealousy. Even in relationships where the sexual element has subsided completely, there might still be a very strong bond of loyalty and an increasing sense of "partnership" which supersedes the sex.

Book to read:

- *Making Gay Relationships Work - a handbook for male couples* by Terry Sanderson (Other Way Press).

This is the well-known term for male prostitutes. It became very popular in tabloid newspapers in the eighties because it embraced all the topics their sick readers found titillating, such as: homosexuality, paedophilia, Aids, child abuse and so on.

Boys who sell sex are common all over the world. Usually the sole motivation is money; in the third world this may be all they have to trade. But sometimes it's a way for young men to explore their sexuality without committing themselves. ("I'm no poof – I only do it for the cash".) There are lurid tales of young runaways from the provinces being picked up as they arrive at London railway stations and then forced to become rent boys. That might be the case, but then again it might just be a tabloid fantasy.

So long as people treat each other respectfully, there is no reason why a money-for-sex transaction should be a sordid one. But because it's against the law, there are bound to be abuses. Be cautious, whichever end of the deal you're on – particularly with safer sex considerations. Sadly, research has shown that a large number of rent boys are HIV positive.

In America the term for rent-boys is "hustlers".

RIDE A COCK HORSE

This is simply sitting on the cock of your partner and "riding" him as a variation of anal intercourse. You can do it laying down, sitting in a chair or, for the more athletic, standing up. The man who is doing the fucking stands up while naked, his partner – who is similarly naked (at least from the waist down) then puts his arms round his lover's neck and wraps his legs round his waist. The cock then fits snugly into the arse. It takes a strong man to maintain this for very long – and do the thrusting as well.

Condoms should always be used for penetrative sex.

Anilingus or oral-anal contact has become much more popular since the advent of the mucky video. Until then, most people would have considered an invitation to "Kiss my arse" to be an insult rather than an invitation. Now it seems to be *de rigeur* in most filmed American gay encounters.

There is no doubt that the gentle, subtle stimulation of the arse by a mobile and exploring tongue can give exquisite sensations to both parties. Sometimes it is used as a precursor to anal intercourse and sometimes simply for its own sake. "Sit on my face" or "Eat my ass" is the frequent cry of the hunky models who feature in the aforementioned videos, and off they go, rimming each other for hours on end.

Cleanliness is absolutely essential if you're attracted to this pastime. Although keeping the anus *totally* clean is almost impossible, you must give it a good old scrub before offering your arsehole to someone's loving lips. Rimming is fraught with the possibility of picking up bugs – Hepatitis A and B, many nasty bacteria and, if you're unlucky, internal parasites that will invade your organs and make you extremely ill for a long time. HIV may also pass through this route in some instances.

One answer is to employ a dental dam (q.v.) as a barrier. This piece of rubbery material, a bit like Clingfilm but less likely to stick to itself, is used as a sort of condom for the tongue. You get most of the sensations but none of the bacteria and viruses.

The same objections apply to oral shields as do to condoms. They are a hassle to use, they interrupt the flow of action and interfere with spontaneity. If you're at the height of passion, the cheeks are parted invitingly and you're itching to get your face in there, it might be a bit of a downer to call a halt and start searching your bedside drawers for a an oral sheath. However, that must be better than spending weeks in isolation with your face a lurid yellow colour and your energy levels at minus 10.

Rimming can be achieved in a number of positions. The person to be rimmed can bend over on hands and knees, causing the cheeks to part. This can allow particularly deep penetration. Or he can lay on his back with legs thrown over his chest, thereby exposing the arse. He might squat over the face of the rimmer, which can be pleasant. The rimmer can sit on the edge of a sofa or chair, while the recipient lays in front of the chair on his back, then swings his legs upwards, opening them to create a Y shape, into the crux of which his partner can bury his face.

Mutual rimming in the sixty-nine position is possible, too.

ROMANCE

The concept of romantic love is European in origin and was unknown in other cultures until imported via films and books. Romance sits uneasily sometimes with gay men. The tradition of depersonalised and instantly available sex is so deeply ingrained in our community that the prospect of "dating" someone and getting to know them a little before putting our cock in their mouth seems almost bizarre to some people. I think this is a shame. We deprive ourselves of much fun and excitement by getting each other into bed (or up an alley or in a loo-stall) before we've even exchanged names.

I'm not suggesting that we embrace the whole heterosexual bit – after all, the desire for hot, anonymous sex can occasionally be most pressing – but sometimes it would be nice to have a candlelit dinner, a few romantic phone calls and so on in order to build the anticipation of the erotic event which will eventually follow.

It would also allow us to screen out those people who we don't actually like very much. It has become something of a joke between gay people that occasionally you'll pick someone up in a drunken haze, have sex with them and the following morning wake up to wonder: "What the hell was I thinking of?" The big question then becomes: How do I get him out of the flat without having to give him breakfast?

A little prior knowledge and a modicum of restraint, would not only save us from such eventualities, it would maybe help us cut down the risks we take in regard to HIV transmission. Still, I suppose romance isn't something you can legislate about. It either happens or it doesn't.

Of course, there's nothing to stop a sexual encounter being romantic, too. Most gay relationships include, in their early stages, whole days spent in bed together. This gives the opportunity for lots of pleasant romance as well as repeatedly getting your rocks off. If you're planning to do this (go on, treat yourselves), have a bottle of champagne or other good wine in the fridge – you can share this between bouts, during the refractory period (see under that heading). Have delicious nibbles around, too, with lots of sensual things like Belgian chocs, oysters, luxury ice cream. Set up your favourite music, lots of slushy romantic stuff. Cover up all TV sets and radios – the outside world shall not be allowed to impinge as this is an occasion just for the two of you, and the state of the economy or goings on in Bosnia Hercegovina have no part in it. It is pure sensual indulgence in which every part of your body will be pampered and used to excess.

Arrange the lighting so it's flattering (candlelight makes everyone look appealing), and perhaps have a few aromatherapy oils to perfume the air. Have "instant" but good meals (sandwiches from Marks and Sparks, quick-cook pizzas and so on) so that neither of you needs to spoil the atmosphere by spending hours in the kitchen.

You can take showers and baths together. Have clean sheets on the bed and central heating if it's cold. Keep K-Y, condoms, toys, towels, mopping up paper within easy reach. Enjoy.

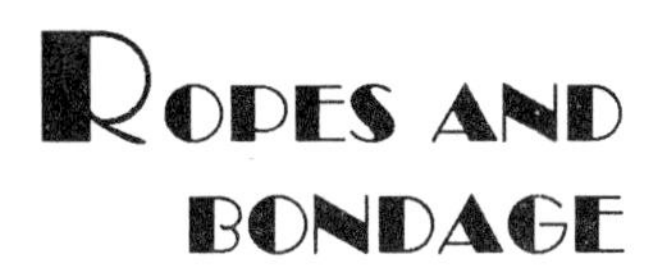

Ropes and Bondage

Many S&M practitioners have a great affection for bondage. It is the ultimate expression of domination, to have someone tied up, hand and foot, and completely at your mercy. Bondage is really best reserved for people who know and trust each other. Allowing yourself to be rendered helpless by a total stranger is asking for trouble. In 1993, five gay men were murdered when they allowed a casual pick up – who turned out to be a homicidal maniac – to handcuff them.

However, if you do know your partner, and have a "bond" of trust with him, then bondage can be great fun. Experts in the art know a lot about tying people up in elaborate ways, with their arms and legs behind them, trussed like a chicken, or often tied to the bed so that they can be sexually "abused" with no power to stop the "abuser". Sometimes whips and tawse (a sort of miniature cat o' nine tails) are employed to flagellate the bound person.

As part of the ritual humiliation, sometimes people are bound (and gagged) and left for long periods in this state of immobility. The master returns at his convenience and does whatever he likes to the slave – the more depraved the better.

Those who are into S&M in a big way know when to stop. They know exactly how tight to tie the ropes, whether a person can tolerate a particular gag for any period of time, and how to tell if the person wants to call a halt.

Often there is an element of begging and pleading from the slave, so it is important that the master knows when it's part of the scene and when it is a genuine desire to stop. Pre-arranged signals are useful here.

Real enthusiasts don't just use ropes for bondage, but also straight-jackets, bandages, handcuffs and anything they can find laying around the house, like neck-ties.

People can be tied to posts, over barrels and suspended from the ceiling (once again, extreme care should be taken to ensure than no-one's airway is restricted and there is no undue pressure on their chest or abdomen).

Rough trade

The concept of "rough trade" is about as politically incorrect as it can be, stinking, as it does, of "classism".

This is how to goes: some over-privileged sophisticate picks up someone from the "lower orders" in order to satisfy a craving for brutal and primitive sexual activity. MPs, clergymen, literary figures, minor aristocracy and others with an inflated sense of their own importance will sometimes be caught out cruising such places as Chelsea barracks, hoping for a quickie with a guardsman. Pillars of the establishment will hang around building sites hoping to tempt some scruffy navvy to drop his keks in return for a wad of bank notes.

To qualify as rough trade, you have to be working class, ignorant, uncouth, shabbily dressed, vulgar and have a big knob. It is this last qualification which is most important. The kind of upper-class Herberts who seek out sex across the class barriers want to be roughly handled by some yokel with no manners and with more than he can handle between his legs. All this is very interesting from a psychological point of view: why do these people, who appear to have everything, want to be abused by their "inferiors"? What is it that makes the effete baronet want to be fondled by the horny-handed workman? A good example of this thinking can be found in E. M. Forster's excruciating novel *Maurice* although the hero of the piece does try to imbue his gamekeeper lover with some semblance of dignity. Forster is credited with the immortal line: "I want to love a strong young man of the lower classes and be loved by him, even hurt by him"

The composer Tchaikovsky had an affair with a taxi driver. The late Lord Boothby, a man of enormous pomposity and egotism (described by biographers as a "promiscuous homosexual" with a penchant for the "serving classes"), is said to have consorted with the gangster Ronnie Kray (and they don't come much rougher than that). D. H. Lawrence, author of Lady Chatterley's Lover has been quoted as saying: "I believe the nearest I have come to perfect love was with a young coal miner when I was about sixteen."

I suppose the seeking out of rough trade is no more dehumanising than any other fetish, and if there is a modicum of wealth redistribution at the end of the transaction, it might even have something going for it.

Book to read:

- *Maurice* by E. M. Forster

A very popular fetish substance which can be fashioned in to all kinds of interesting garments which lift, separate and display. You can get T-shirts, vests, jeans, chaps, gloves, suits, hoods, restraints.

Because of its stretch properties rubber can give emphasis in places which few other materials can touch.

Power and the relinquishing of power; forcing and yielding; activity and passivity, all these elements are combined in even the mildest forms of sex. Whether it consists of nibbling the ear of a slightly resisting partner, or the full-scale enactment of an S&M "scene", the principle is the same: domination and submission. When this inevitable element of sexual contact is taken to its logical extreme it can become a motivation and end in itself.

Although the Marquis de Sade and Chevalier Leopold von Sacher-Masoch never met, their names are inextricably linked in the term sado-masochism. De Sade epitomised and popularised the idea of sexual gratification through the inflicting of pain and humiliation. Sacher-Masoch, on the other hand, was the Viennese writer who came to represent the other end of the spectrum – sexual gratification through receiving pain.

Sado-Masochism has been explored over the years by those who are particularly excited at the prospect of totally dominating their partner and those who wish to be completely powerless and submissive.

Gay men have always recognised and exploited these desires. Since our sexuality was more liberated we have been more receptive and open about these activities, and have explored the possibilities much more freely. The American writer Wayne R. Dynes described it this way: "Seemingly objective presentations of the nature of S/M almost invariably slight the less tangible elements that are of supreme importance to those who are seriously committed. In the view of some who are experienced in the scene the real appeal of S/M is that it promotes a state of consciousness that transcends ego. Such 'egoless' states are inherently blissful. Moreover, participants have the sense that they are involved in a form of magic or alchemy. In a state of perfect trust, their 'vibrations' become perfectly attuned to one another, and blows that would be normally unwelcome are transmuted into a choreography of pleasure."

Slaves and their masters play out scenes of ritual humiliation, of degradation and pain and of abuse. We have looked at some of the many forms that these desires can take (see Ropes and bondage; Knots; Leashes; Top Man; Fetishes; Tattoos, Piercing).

S&M enthusiasts have a very lively social scene where they can dress in fetish gear (particularly leather), and find others of like mind who are prepared to help them live out their deepest fantasies. Sometimes these fantasies involve torture, whipping, caning, verbal abuse, boot licking, spanking, bondage and genital piercing. For the most experienced S&Mers these games are played in a way in which no-one is seriously damaged or injured. The pain is kept to a safe level and much of the physical abuse is simulated.

The law is unclear about what exactly we are permitted to do with our own bodies. A notorious court case – the Spanner trial – decided that there were limits to what individuals are permitted to do to each other, even if no real damage is inflicted and it is with consent. We cannot always legally consent to being 'assaulted'.

S&Mers, then, must be cautious about what records they keep of their games. No videos, diaries, photos or written records should be kept that might later prove incriminating.

Because S&M scenes are personal creations, they can be tailored to fit exactly the requirements of the participants. If particular thrills are gained from the master calling his slave every filthy and disgusting name he can lay tongue to, then that can be the focus. If a more subtle kind of humiliation is required, it can be gained from, perhaps, having the slave engage in menial and debasing tasks. Sometimes the scene is drawn out over hours or days. Partners may be living out their S&M scene while they are at your dinner party! If one man is constantly criticising or belittling his partner in front of friends, it may be that (a) their relationship is heading for the rocks or (b) that they've agreed beforehand that the Master has permission to torment his Slave in this publicly humiliating way.

The sexual thrill in S&M is often gained from thoughts and fantasies and ritualised beatings rather than from direct genital stimulation, which is why its exploration is frequently recommended as a tool for safer sex. So long as no blood is drawn (and if it is, it should be treated cautiously), and condoms are applied if penetration is going to be part of the scene, all should be well.

For beginners, care should be taken with the use of ropes and other bondage equipment. Signals to stop must always be pre-arranged and heeded. Trust is an essential element for the enjoyment of S&M.

There are different views of S&M, of course. Some people consider that what it represents for gay people is really their self-loathing. They want to be punished for being gay, they want to be humiliated because, secretly, that's what they think they deserve. There is little doubt that many gay people feel badly about their sexuality and perhaps S&M is a way for them to funnel those feelings of self-contempt. But, goes the argument, it also *reinforces* the idea that gay sex is disgusting and needs to be expressed as pain and humiliation.

But sexual desire is not always politically correct. What people make of their feelings is ultimately up to them. However, just because S&M has such a high profile in the gay community does not mean that you have to be interested in it. It is still very much a minority sport and no-one should feel pressured to be involved in activities that they don't really enjoy.

In fact, of all the people I've ever spoken to about their sex lives, only a small handful have expressed any real interest in inflicting or receiving pain during sex. For most people, S&M is just a matter of "if it turns you on, fine, but it does nothing for me."

Group to contact:

- SM Gays, BM SM Gays, London WC1N 3XX (send s.a.e.).

SAFER SEX

Note that I use the term "safer" sex rather than "safe" sex. I do not believe there is such a thing as one hundred per cent "safe" sex. The whole point about sex is that there is a risk involved. It might not always be a physical risk (although often it is), it might be an emotional risk. A sexual encounter involves opening up our psyche in a way that few other activities do. We can just as easily have our feelings and our self-esteem hurt by a disastrous sexual episode, as we can our arse or cock.

The phrase safer sex relates to the avoidance of infection with HIV, the virus that can lead to AIDS. Generally it can be defined as an attempt to prevent the bodily fluids of one person getting into the body of another.

Safer sex practices include finding alternatives to penetration, or, if penetration is going to take place, ensuring the use of condoms. Most of the HIV and AIDS information and education groups have leaflets which give the latest findings on the relative safety of individual sexual acts – and also suggest alternatives to the more dangerous practices. If you aren't practising safer sex, then it's time to start. Recent research shows that the rate of HIV infection is beginning to rise among gay men again, particularly those under 25. It's time to start having more respect for ourselves and each other in order to stem the growth of this horrible disease (see Self-Esteem).

Group to contact:

- Terrence Higgins Trust on 0171-242 1010.

Book to read:

- The Guide to Gay Sex Safely - Peter Tatchell (Cassell)

The Sambia are a tribe in Papua New Guinea whose men appear to believe that swallowing semen is an essential step to becoming masculine, and they spend a great deal of time sucking each other off as part of a prolonged transition into adulthood. I'm surprised that Papua New Guinea has not become a favourite gay holiday destination on a par with Mykonos and Gran Canaria.

Sauna

Saunas – those horrendous steam baths – originated in Finland. Because they are so uncomfortable, it is assumed that they bestow some kind of health benefit. I'm not yet convinced that sweating it out in a glorified garden shed does anything but make you feel as though you are going to die. No wonder people think it's done them good, it feels great just getting out!

But, of course, because you are required to discard your clothing and sit about with nothing to do but look between each other's legs, saunas have become associated with sex. And because – in Britain at least – mixed sex sessions are rare, saunas have become homo-eroticised. Municipal saunas are quite often the haunt of gay people on the lookout for a sweaty afternoon. A similar idea, the Turkish bath, also became the haunt of those seeking filthiness as well as cleanliness. In Roman times the public baths were an important part of the social framework. Naturally only men were allowed to use them and as pleasure was a ruling principle in those times, the boys not only negotiated politics, they also got fruity when the steam rose.

Scat

Scat comes from scatology – the study of excrement. It is sometimes called coprophilia. It means playing with and, in some extreme instances, eating shit during a sexual episode. Usually this is part of S&M procedures, and the ultimate humiliation for the master is to make his slave eat shit. This is extremely dangerous. One man's meat is another man's poison – especially when it has passed through his alimentary canal. Unless you have a death wish, don't eat shit under any circumstances.

Other variations are the master squatting over the slave and shitting on him or simply smearing shit over his body. This has its dangers, too, if there are cuts, scratches or sores on the skin. Anyway, I think scat is more talked about than practised, and this is confirmed by statistics from Project Sigma which indicate that only 3 per cent of gay men have tried scat during their sex life, and none of them had done it in the month before the survey was conducted. This seems to indicate that a very small number of gay men are curious about scat and want to try it at least once, but very few repeat the experience.

Schoolboy sex

British public schools (which, paradoxically, are actually private) are notorious hotbeds of homosexual experimentation. The ingredients are all in place for a heady mix: all those young men with their burgeoning sexual feelings, the absence of females, the long, lonely nights in the dorm and the hero-worship of older boys. According to the large-scale survey 'Sexual Behaviour in Britain', boys who went to boarding school are twice as likely to have had a homosexual experience (14 per cent compared with 6 per cent) at some time in their lives. Though boarding school gives greater opportunity for sexual experimentation, the report suggests it does not influence adult sexual orientation.

Writing about school days homosexuality in *The Daily Telegraph*, Henry Dimbleby, who once went to Eton, says that despite denials, homosexuality in boarding schools is still very common. He wrote:

"The mechanics of making a pass at another boy are as arcane as any public school ritual. The consequences of being caught, which inevitable adds a certain *frisson* to the encounters, also necessitate meticulous caution. You must always be able to claim, if challenged, that your behaviour has been misunderstood. Once the subject has committed himself to a degree where he could not expose you without exposing himself the tension breaks and you can proceed in a relatively 'normal' fashion. Bizarrely this performance is reinacted with each encounter: because there is a guilt and fear associated with the trysts, you can never assume that a boy will acquiesce once would be willing to do so again. Sex between schoolboys tend to occur with the full consent of all concerned and involve fairly harmless fumblings. One case during my time at Eton was when an older boy went to a junior's room one night asking for help with his maths. He was 17, the junior 14. He sat on the side of the bed – it was nearly time for lights out – and rested his textbook on the junior's lap, with his hand supporting it from below. At any stage the junior could have moved or said he wanted to go to sleep and he would have left. Alternatively if the junior had accused him of making a pass, he could have denied it."

He also relates the experiences of a friend of his who reported the frequent sighting at rugby matches of an older boy, standing on the sidelines, with two younger boys at either side of him. Each of the younger boys had a hand in the older boy's pockets.

Such institutions also seem to attract more than their fair share of paedophiles to the academic staff.

Scissors

This is a sexual position for anal intercourse. The partner who is to be fucked lays on his side, while the person who is going to do the fucking puts on a condom and lays in the same position behind him. The receptive partner opens his legs (like a pair of scissors) and allows access. For the sake of comfort, the receptive partner can support his leg in this raised position by bending his knee and holding it up with his arm.

SEAFOOD

Delightful American euphemism for sucking off sailors.

SELF-ESTEEM

Self-esteem has been defined as "a sense of self-worth coming from within yourself rather than being dependent on the goodwill of others."

Sexual self-esteem means being able to enjoy sex without feelings of guilt, shame or anxiety about failure. If you don't like yourself very much (low self-esteem), others will find it hard to like you either. If you feel ashamed of, or are dissatisfied with, your body, then you will find it difficult to share it with other people.

A secure sexual identity is often difficult for gay people to achieve. For many, sexual self-esteem will have been severely damaged early in childhood. Remember the lapel badge that read: "I am the person my mother warned me about"? Well, if even our mother told us when, as a child she sat us on her knee, that homosexuality was mad, bad, sick or undesirable, then it is unlikely that we will have survived to adulthood feeling totally comfortable about our gayness.

These feelings of guilt and shame which cling to our sexuality are called 'internalised homophobia'. With effort it can be overcome, and we can begin to feel good about loving our own sex. The best way to challenge self-oppression and consequent loss of self-esteem is to mix with positive gay people who are at ease with their orientation. It's amazing what a good role model can do!

Book to read:

- *Assertively Gay: How to Build Gay Self-Esteem* by Terry Sanderson published by The Other Way Press.

SEMEN

See under Cum. Other words for semen are seminal fluid, come, cream, gism, goo, juice, load, love juice, man oil, spunk, water of life and whipped cream.

SHAVING

Some men gain great erotic pleasure from shaving their own and other people's bodies. Naturally, if a friend wants you to take the hair off his private places, you get to explore those places pretty intimately. A wet shave gives you the opportunity of tickling your partner with a soft but prickly brush. You can cover his parts with shaving foam, and then out comes the razor.

Naturally it will be necessary for you to hold the cock if you are shaving the pubes, and naturally you would have to pull the cheeks of the arse apart if you are shaving a particularly hairy specimen in that area.

We've already explored (under Hair) the aesthetic reasons for some men wanting to shave more than their face. I was talking to someone recently who had been to the last Gay Olympics in America and had discovered from one of the athletes that the drains had become blocked by the huge amount of bodily hair that had been flushed down the sinks and plug holes. All those perfect bodies needed to be seen in their sculpted glory, and hair simply got in the way. I expect the barber, whether professional or amateur, actually paid his customers in that instance to shave away the pesky bodily hair.

Anyone who has shaved their pubes though, will tell you that when the hair grows back it can be very uncomfortable. Having stubble in your basket can create the most inconvenient and embarrassing itching. Unless you're prepared to spend a week to ten days scratching at your crotch from morning until night, then don't shave anywhere below the belt.

Group to contact:

- Body Shavers Group. Send an s.a.e. to BSG, Suite 116, Victor Tower, Birmingham B7 5BW.

SHUDO

Shudo was part of the philosophy adopted by the Japanese samurai warriors in the eighteenth and nineteenth century. It involved the future warrior, as an adolescent, first being loved by an older man, then himself loving a younger man before eventually marrying a woman. We've already considered "situational homosexuality" – the sort that takes place in prisons and monasteries and other one-sex establishments, and "constitutional" homosexuality – which seems to be an innate part of some people's character. Shudo seems to have been "philosophical" homosexuality – a decision to have sex with other men as an aesthetic statement.

Homosexuality was commonplace and accepted throughout Japanese culture until early in the twentieth century.

SIGNALS

A lot gay people like to think they have a sort of invisible antenna on their heads which allows them to pick up signals from other gay men. Sometimes it feels that way when you suddenly meet someone in a neutral situation (such as at work) and immediately there is something about them that says; "I'm gay and I might be interested".

The give-away signals might be to do with their body language – the way they look at you, the way they stand, the way they speak. Often it is very subtle, and no-one but you seems to have noticed. You might then feel like "signalling" back, by holding his gaze that fraction too long, or by making semi-flirtatious comments that wouldn't be discernible to half-asleep straights.

Back before the gay community was organised and you had to go to dangerous lengths to meet sex partners, it was traditional for gay men to wear a pinkie ring on their little finger. In traditional "ring language" this signifies a confirmed bachelor. If any suspicious straight challenged you about the wearing of a pinkie, you'd simply say "Oh my Grandmother left it to me in her will and it just won't fit any other finger."

Then there is the more overt system of signalling through handkerchiefs worn by gay men in their back pockets. On which side you wore them was supposed to indicate whether you were "active" or "passive", the colours were to announce what kind of sex you preferred. This idea was adapted from the South Sea islands, where the natives developed a complex sexual signalling system with the use of flowers – a flower behind the left ear means married, behind the right ear means "try me." Different kinds of flowers indicated different preferences. On the island of Martinique in the French Caribbean sexual signals can be given through the tying of knots in the Madras head scarf. which is worn there. One knot means 'my heart is free', two knots means 'my heart is engaged but you could try your luck'; three knots means 'my heart is taken and I am strictly not available'; four knots means 'anyone who tries is most welcome'.

SIXTY-NINING

Mutual oral sex is termed sixty-nining (sometimes also called by its French name *soixante-neuf*) because the position of the two bodies could be said to resemble the figures 69. It is an extremely popular activity with gay men, and can be attempted in all kinds of positions. The most popular is where on partner lies flat on the bed and the other kneels, reverse way round, on all fours over him. For the adventurous and athletic, one partner can stand against a wall, while the other does a hand stand. Draped upside down over the back of a sofa is also quite a pleasant way to sixty-nine.

Because the cock always goes into the mouth "upside down" – that is to say with the sensitive underneath part of the knob on the roof of the mouth – it is difficult to give this the same attention with the tongue as in one-at-a-time oral sex. Still that is small price to pay for such an attractive and exciting experience.

SMEGMA

Smegma (sometimes also called cock cheese) is a fatty, oily substance secreted by the sebaceous glands of the foreskin and the neck and glans of the penis. Smegma has a distinctive odour, rather like over-ripe *Pont L'Eveque*. It might accumulate if you don't keep yourself clean 'down there'.

Sodomy

Sodomy, of course, is a biblical term, derived from that infamous city of the plain, Sodom, which (according to Genesis 14, 18 and 19) was destroyed by God in a hail of fire and brimstone. It was there that the male inhabitants apparently wanted to "know" a (male) angel who was visiting Lot's house. It all hinges on what people mean by "to know" in this sense. Some traditionalist interpreters of the Bible (commonly known as the Jesus-in-Jackboots Brigade) say it means that the Sodomites wanted to shag the angel. Those of a more liberal persuasion simply think that God destroyed Sodom and Gomorra because the citizens were not very hospitable. Those of us of a rational persuasion think the whole thing is a load of bollocks that no sensible person would give the time of day to.

Whatever the truth, the story of Sodom has been the bane of gay people's lives for the past two thousand years.

In the twelfth century those men caught fucking each other were charged in the ecclesiastical courts with a crime called *sodomia imperfecta.* If priests were found guilty of this offence they would be confined to a monastery. Needless to say, they would then have almost unlimited opportunity for further activities of the *sodomia imperfecta* type, (or 'going up the cassock' as it was known to connoisseurs).

Spanish fly

Among the legendary aphrodisiacs, Spanish Fly is often listed. This is how it is made: the cantharis beetle is collected and anaesthetised. The comatose insect is then placed in an oven where it crumbles to dust. This dust is the chief ingredient of the love potion we are talking about. However, the effects on sexual functioning is not always the one that might be hoped for. By irritating the urethra, it can cause all kinds of genito-urinary problems, not least of which are painful erections which can sometimes be prolonged for hours – or even days.

If anyone offers you Spanish Fly, I suggest you don't take it. It's unlikely to be the real thing anyway, but if it is, it will probably make you very ill.

Spanking

Sometimes referred to as 'slap and tickle', spanking is surprisingly popular, and is probably the mildest and most widely practised form of sexual punishment. Those who are into spanking in a big way will find that there are endless books, films, telephone lines and stories to pander to their desires. Usually these scenarios revolve around nasty schoolmasters spanking naughty boys, and their popularity might have something to do with the English school system and its predilection for slippers, canes and "Take your pants down boy!"

An example of this is contained in the book *A History of Wimbledon College* by Anthony Poole and is reproduced here for its historical significance, of course, and not for any prurient purpose:

"Punishment was dealt out at two set times during breaks. A short (occasionally long) queue of boys gathered outside the respective master's study door, the wiser ones warming heir hands on the central heating pipes, and one by one they knocked and were invited in. It was then their part to ask 'Please may I have (x number of) ferulas?' (A ferula is a one-foot long, leather-covered rubber strap, somewhat resembling the sole of a shoe). The details noted in the punishment book, his hand duly whacked with stunning report, the poor unfortunate duly had to say 'Thank You'."

I gave spanking a try once with an *aficionado*, and I have to say that by the end of the first half hour, my bottom was beginning to feel extremely sore, and I was getting bored with the repetitive nature of the exercise. My companion didn't seem interested in taking things further, and simply wanted me to tell him lurid tales of school punishments, while he bashed my buttocks.

I came away from the encounter with a pretty low opinion of spanking as a means of passing the time.

SPORTSWEAR

The gym culture which has grown up in gay circles has brought with it the large-scale eroticisation of sporting clothes. Tight athletic vests, split-up-the-side running shorts, the ubiquitous jock strap as well as track suits that cling in the important areas. There are Lycra cycling shorts for those who can't ride bikes, and jogging shoes for people who wouldn't be seen dead running through the streets. All these items, because of their association with young, vibrant and active young men, are used ruthlessly as sexual attractants. They are increasingly becoming essential items for erotic encounters, and fetishes are developing for some styles of shorts or well-cut vests that accentuate the hard-earned muscles.

According to *The Sun,* ex-Government minister David Mellor enjoyed making love in a Chelsea football strip, and there is no reason why you shouldn't either if footballers are your bag. The attractiveness of cricketers, too, has increased considerably in recent years, and their white flannels (with protective "box" beneath) can be exceptionally lovely.

Australian football requires the wearing of extremely brief and ludicrously tight shorts, but strangely they are not very pleasant to look at.

Rugby players, too, have their fans. Rugby League, with its extreme violence, is for those who like big, beefy, broken-nosed beasts. For some reason the shorts are of a silky material which displays everything most satisfactorily. Rugby Union, on the other hand, has prettier boys but less revealing shorts. Rugby scrums, which give the players an opportunity to shamelessly handle each others bottoms, make good homo-erotic television.

Group to contact:

- Locker 92, for men interested in sportswear and personal fitness, PO Box 92, Wokingham, Berks RG11 9DE.

Strippers/ Stripping

Male strippers are back in fashion in a big way. Women now demand "hen parties" at which there is usually a drag artist and a troupe of hunky strippers, all of whom make a good living from these events. Their services are also constantly in demand in gay pubs and clubs. Politically correct women would say that this is a long overdue table-turning exercise on men, who for years have been treating female bodies as sex objects. But the women who actually go to these hen-nights would argue that there is no political statement in their attendance – they have simply shrugged the shackles from their sexuality, and admitted that they, too, like to look at men as sexual objects.

I'm not sure whether it is lust, revenge or both. The only thing that is certain from all this is that men with big cocks, bouffant hair and names like Big Joe generally can't dance.

The position in the gay community is different. Nobody doubts that the strippers are there for no other reason than to titillate and excite. They aren't engaged for the kind of sniggering humiliation which often seems to be the case at hen nights.

But pleasant though it may be to see some well-developed hunk strip off his clothes to the sound of throbbing music, there is usually a sense of frustration at not being able to take him home to have your wilful way. Sometimes it is also excruciatingly embarrassing when the man in question has little sense of erotic presentation.

This is where D-I-Y stripping comes into its own. A slow undressing can make an excellent prelude to love-making. Don't just rip-'em-off and get on with it, make it alluring and enticing. Wear some exciting things beneath the jeans and T-shirt – perhaps a leather jock-strap or thong (but be careful, many of these supposedly erotic undergarments appear ludicrous if they are topped by a pot-belly). Get yourself going with a bit of judicious rubbing, just like the strippers do, in order to make the whole thing seem larger than life.

Some people do a surreptitious strip, in which they pretend that they are unaware that their partner is watching them, but they still take their time about disrobing, carefully folding their clothes so as to drag out the suspense of the final unveiling. Stripping in front of a mirror can give rise to some interesting views for any onlooker. If you have a regular partner, find out what kind of clothing particularly appeals to him and then use those items in your strip routine.

Business suits have taken on sexy connotations for many people. In former days, the traditional image of the business man was of the pompous pin-striped banker with his bowler hat and rolled umbrella. He was far from sexy; indeed, he represented the archetype of frustration and sexual deprivation. Whenever a brothel was raided or a strip joint exposed in *The News of the World*, you can bet your sweet life that the clientele would consist mainly of clergymen, politicians and – you guessed it – businessmen. The first two in the list I can understand – their constant railing against other people's lack of sexual morality, almost inevitably means that their own will be questionable.

But why should businessmen in particular feel the need to relieve themselves with Miss Whiplash types? Why do rent boys get such a good living from the "City gent" classes? Perhaps it's just a desire to break out of the strait-jacket of big business conventionality – and into the strait-jacket provided by Brian the Bondage Boy.

Nowadays, as anyone who regularly commutes in a large city will attest, the attractiveness of businessmen has increased a hundred fold. For one thing, they seem younger, their suits are generally more stylish and, because they've all been on courses telling them how important "power dressing" is, they present themselves very well.

Many gay men are turned on by this almost artificial perfection (expensive hair-cut, clean-shaven, beautiful skin, carefully chosen ties, designer shoes and suits that are tailored to present the body the best advantage). Besides the obvious appeal of the personal power some of these men project (often it is all an illusion created by the ruthless exploitation of the psychological effects of aforementioned power dressing), there is the also the desire among many gay men to get at the seat of that power (so to speak), and experience it intimately.

There are even male strippers who specialise in the Wall Street look. They carefully disrobe, first taking off the silk tie, then the elegantly contoured jacket, and after that the Italian shirt. At this point they will have revealed a magnificent chest, but they will also have destroyed the mystique of the office dreamboat—without his suit and tie he is nothing, so the pants and undies can be dispensed with very rapidly.

The fantasy of the thrusting executive is, perhaps, the most fragile of them all. Indeed, those who dream of ravishing a handsome businessman over his desk would, perhaps, prefer him to keep his suit on during the proceedings. Once it has been discarded, the dream is ended.

Group to contact:

- Suit and Tie Society (a group for men who like that sort of thing). PO Box 59, Midland Road, Derby DE1 9PA.

Syphilis

Syphilis is one of the most dangerous venereal diseases and because the symptoms vary so widely between people, it is not always recognised. It can, in its final stages, cripple or even kill its victims.

Syphilis is generally passed on by sexual contact. You can't catch it from a toilet seat, or a beer glass or a door handle. The bacteria that cause syphilis can thrive in any warm, moist area of the body, so they can enter through the genitals, the throat, the anus or the mouth. It doesn't need prolonged contact – just a brush with the bacteria is enough to let it into the body.

The first sign of syphilis is the appearance of a sore, which is about the size of a baked bean and shows itself about four weeks after infection. If the bacterium has entered the body in a concealed place – like up your arse or through your tonsils – you might not even notice it. If untreated, the sore will disappear after a week or so and you will enter the second stage, which is characterised by a rash. This rash might appear anywhere on the body, even on the palms of the hands or the soles of the feet. In some people the rash is dramatic and livid, in others it might be so discreet that it passes unnoticed. Sometimes also at this stage, but not always, there is a mild fever and some people lose a little of their hair. Within two weeks the second stage will have ended and at this point the bacterium goes into hiding within the body. It might remain there, inactivated, for the rest of your life, but then again it might reappear to enter the third or "tertiary" stage, when it could attack the heart or the nervous system.

If caught in the earlier stages, though, syphilis can be successfully treated with antibiotics. If in doubt, get checked out.

Where to get help:

- Department of Genito-urinary Medicine at your local hospital. Can't find it? Look under V.D. in the phone book.

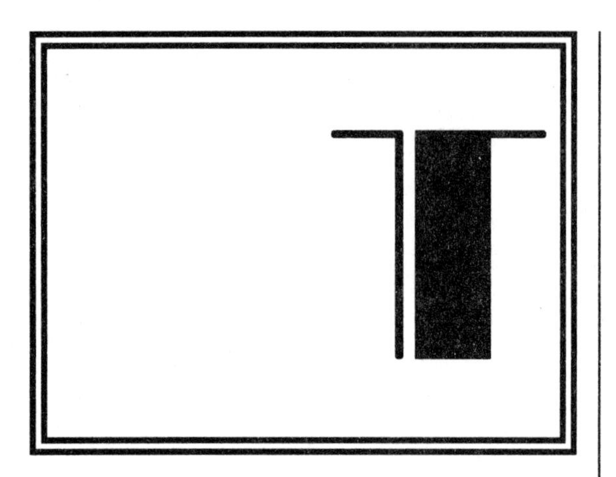

Talking Dirty

Dirty talk can be sexy, it can also be excruciatingly embarrassing. Some people like it, others find it a complete turn-off. If the extent of your dirty talk is what you've learned from your videos ("You like that dontcha?"; "Oh yeah, oh yeah"; "suck it! suck it!" etc.,) than it is likely to be pretty boring. However, as an overture to the real thing it can be very exciting. I remember once dancing close to someone I'd met in a club. As we hugged on the dance floor he put his mouth to my ear and told me in graphic detail what he intended to do when we were alone together. If I hadn't been already on the point of collapse from drinking too much, I would have fainted from the excitement.

The tone of voice, too, is important. It's no use talking mucky in a monotone. It has to have passion. If it's going to resemble an I-speak-your-weight-machine then stick to grunts and groans. You have to sound as though you mean it and it has to be free from embarrassment. It can occasionally be issued in the form of a threat or abuse ("I'm going to fuck you so hard, you'll see stars, you filthy slut!") or it can be romantic and reassuring ("I love you sucking my cock, you have such a wonderful, warm mouth.")

Elocution lessons are not required for enunciating this kind of poetry.

Tattoos

There's no doubt that tattoos are sexy to some people – to the wearer *and* the viewer. They are usually associated with prisoners, Hell's Angels, skinheads, soldiers and sailors. Traditionally, they have represented a kind of male bonding – the two friends staggering drunkenly into the tattoo parlour and daring each other to have a more outrageous one applied – and so have always had an appeal to gay men. It can be quite arousing to see a tattoo on a well-muscled lover – even if it does say "I love Doris".

But tattoos have become fashionable. Madonna has one, and so does Cher. Style magazines laud them and the gay community has taken them up in a big way. So what if you want to have a tattoo yourself? How do you go about it?

The first thing is to think very carefully before going ahead. Don't do it in a fit of bravado. Make an appointment a week ahead so that you have a cooling off period. Tattoos are almost impossible to remove without painful and expensive laser treatments or skin grafts, and despite what the brochures from plastic surgery clinics might say, these treatments almost always leave scarring.

Many health authorities place removal of tattoos at a low priority, reasoning that if you paid to have it put on, you can pay to have it taken off. So, once you've got one, you're going to have to live with it, or a lot of unsightly scars. Some tattoo artists insist that their customers sign a disclaimer that they are not under 18, not under the influence of alcohol and realise that the tattoo is for life.

If, despite all this, you decide to go ahead, choose the design carefully. Start with something small and unobtrusive. You'd be well-advised not to have a declaration of undying love addressed to a particular name – remember Doris? Choose something that won't embarrass you at a later date. After all, a tattoo is likely to last much longer than a relationship.

Where you have the tattoo placed is entirely up to you – wherever there is skin, tattoos can be applied. Some people like to have them in hidden places that only their sexual partners will see. Most responsible tattooists will not tattoo the genitals and some won't touch the face. As a deterrent, one that I know of charges double price for necks and hands.

Tattooing is a specialised art best not attempted by amateurs. Go to a reputable and registered artist who looks after his equipment and sterilises it properly. Ask to see the sterilised needles in their unopened packet before the artist commences work, that way you know they haven't been used on anyone else.

A tattoo consists of special inks and dyes which are injected under the skin surface and are permanently trapped by collagen. The process is achieved with needles driven by something like a sewing machine which punctures the skin at three thousand jabs a minute. Some people feel that the pain involved in tattooing is exciting, an essential part of the whole experience. Others who've had it done liken it to the burning of red hot daggers. Analgesic creams can be applied beforehand.

Nowadays you can also get temporary tattoos, what were called 'transfers' in my childhood. You can apply them and wash them off at will. Perhaps a better bet than the real thing.

Transfers available from

- Clone Zone, 39 Bloom Street, Manchester M1 3LY

Teeth can add an awful lot of appeal to a face, so if you've got good teeth, look after them, and if you haven't, visit an cosmetic dentist and have them seen to. Teeth are also essential for nibbling, that delicious aspect of foreplay which involves gently biting the earlobes, nipples, buttocks etc. Care must always be taken not to break the skin, as nasty infections can follow from human bites.

You might also be interested to know that America's Academy of Dentistry has announced that kissing is good for the teeth. They discovered that the anticipation of a kiss increases the flow of saliva in the mouth, showering our ivories with enamel building calcium and phosphorous. The British Dental Association agrees and says that saliva is the most important factor in stopping our teeth rotting. However, the British Dental Association, lacking the romance of its American counterpart, says that the same effect can be obtained from chewing an elastic band.

Perhaps, but it's not half as much fun.

TELEPHONE SEX

Judging by the amount of advertising, these premium-rate phone lines must do a roaring trade. Aural sex, particularly over the phone, is obviously very popular. Listening to these pre-recorded stories, as opposed to a live person, has the advantage that you can wank away without having to interrupt the fantasy by listening to someone sounding bored or eating an apple or whatever. The downside is that they're bloody expensive. This is one sexual activity where it pays to suffer from premature ejaculation.

Of course, if you are parted from your loved one because of business or whatever, you can still keep in touch by phone, talk dirty to each other over the wires and continue to be intimate over the BT or Mercury lines (Mercury is cheaper over long distances). Remember, though, that uttering obscenities down the phone is illegal. But now comes the newest novelty – videophones. For a relatively modest cost, you can see what your lover looks like – and more importantly, what he's doing. Mutual masturbation takes on a whole new meaning. And if you're responding to an advertisement because someone has promised that they have ten inches, you can demand that they prove it before you arrange a meeting.

The telephone handset, too has been used as a dildo before now, so having sex over the telephone can be almost as graphic as being there.

TESTICULAR CANCER

Testicular cancer is the most common form of cancer in young men, occurring mostly in those aged between 15 and 49. However, it is still quite rare with just over 1,000 new cases a year and about 150 deaths in the UK. The good news is that it is also one of the most curable cancers. Over 90 per cent of patients make a full recovery and when the disease is caught at an early stage, survival is almost 100 per cent.

The first sign of this cancer is usually a swelling of one of the testicles. Occasionally there may be a dull ache or, even more seldom, acute pain.

It's important for all men to examine themselves frequently and seek help if they find any irregularities. Bear in mind that the shape and size of bollocks varies widely between individuals, so it is wise to make sure you feel them regularly so that you are familiar with your own particular shape – it's then easier to judge if they've changed. Examination is best undertaken just after a warm bath or shower, when the muscles in the scrotal sac are more relaxed. Each testicle should be gently examined between the finger and thumb of both hands. Any change (particularly a hardening lump or swelling) should be discussed with your doctor.

While the prospect of dying from this cancer has declined substantially over the past 20 years, the risk of developing it has nearly doubled and figures are still going up. One theory is that increased levels of pollution in food and the atmosphere might have something to do with it. Men born with an undescended testicle have a greater chance of developing testicular cancer. There are several other possible causes of swellings in the testicles, so don't immediately jump to the conclusion that any change is cancer. It might well be epididymitis, a varicocele (varicose vein) or hydrocele. The doctor will put your mind at rest.

TESTOSTERONE

Testosterone is the male hormone, and is a much misunderstood chemical. Many men think that if they could only get a testosterone injection it would make them into the superstud they imagine every other man to be. Well, it would certainly make them more aggressive and it would have an effect on their male sexual characteristics, but it wouldn't necessarily improve their sex life.

Some doctors will readily prescribe testosterone for impotent men, but there is growing evidence that these drugs – like all supposedly aphrodisiac substances – work more through suggestion than actual physical effect. The hard truth is that there is little scientific evidence to prove a link between sexual desire and hormone level.

It's true that if a man's testicles aren't functioning properly, and he is not producing the requisite amount of testosterone, a quick shot of man-juice will effect an improvement, but a man whose equipment is working normally, but who still doesn't have a great libido, can't blame his hormones. The cause is much more likely to be a lack of self-esteem. Yes, the way we see ourselves in relation to others is much more important than hormone levels, when it comes to being a superstud.

If we are depressed, feeling inferior, shy or lacking in self-confidence, we are likely to have problems with our libido. Those who have the best sex are the confident individuals who are outgoing and who believe that they are entitled to everything that's going. If you constantly feel that your sex life is lacklustre, then the way to change it is to become more assertive, more confident in yourself, more extrovert and maybe even a little proud. A tall order, I admit.

Sexual failure is – except for some rare physical problems – all in the mind. If you've eliminated the physical explanations by visiting the doctor, then you have to face up to the harder truths. It takes work and courage to change the way we see ourselves, and often it can only be done over a long period of time. Don't ever give up hope, and never stop trying.

However, for those with a lower than normal level of testosterone (and research shows it to be only 1 per cent of men between 20 and 40, and 5 per cent between 40 and 65), hormone replacement therapy is available. In the USA two drug companies are working to develop a testosterone patch, which works in a similar way to the nicotine patches that help smokers quit. The patch contains a gel composed of fatty lipids and alcohols that facilitate the hormone's penetration of the skin. This model can be worn on the upper arm. The other model needs to be fixed directly on to the scrotum, where the extra-thin skin makes it easier for the hormone to enter the bloodstream.

THREEWAY

Many gay couples like to spice up their love lives by introducing a third party into their bed. Threeways present all kinds of possibilities and combinations of bodily parts. The ability to experience new sensations and sexual roles is enticing, too. But combining in this way can also introduce complications into established relationships.

From what I've learned about threesomes, it seems that in most instances, someone gets left out. Two of the party find that they particularly turn each other on and they tend to start neglecting, or even excluding, the other. Jealousy or resentment quickly arises in these circumstances, and what started out as an exciting idea ends up destroying the relationship. If you're in a gay partnership and considering having a threesome, ensure that your relationship is strong enough to withstand any resentful feelings which might arise.

Organising a threeway with people who don't have any kind of emotional attachment isn't so easy. But if you can manage it, and all three of you are attracted to each other, the sparks can fly.

If you've ever wanted to suck two cocks at once, or be fucked and sucked at the same time, or have both mouth and arse filled simultaneously by cock, then a three way is the only way to do it.

Any combination which you can think of involving three people can be tried in different positions – standing, sitting, laying. There are three cocks, three mouths, three arses, six nipples and lots of other new permutations that can be introduced with the aid of vibrators, dildoes, tables, chairs, step-ladders, ropes, clothing (imagine your little trio dressing up as a sailor, policeman and hard hat workman and then going to it in a threesome!)

Remember, though, any homosexual sex which involves more than two people is illegal in Britain. So only try it on holiday in more civilised countries. And use condoms.

Tits

Tits are usually considered the primary weapon of women in the war to gain the attention of sex partners, but now men are using them as a lure. Working out has developed many men's pectorals to the extent that they often have tits bigger than many women. These are emphasised by the wearing of tight T-shirts. When the advertising has paid dividends and a partner has been enticed by the bulging breasts, the real fun can begin. The sensitive part of the tits are, of course, the nipples, and there is more information under that heading.

Tonguing

The slightly rough texture of the tongue, as well as its natural lubrication, make it an excellent sex tool. Giving sensitive nipples a good, hard lick can be a treat, as can be licking the end of the penis. The trouble is that all those knobbly bits on the tongue are taste buds, and if you're licking something nasty (like a smeggy cock or an unwiped arse) you'll know all about how it tastes. Answer: keep your naughty bits clean for your partner, unless specifically requested otherwise.

Tourism (1)

Sex tourism has increased in popularity as travel has become easier and cheaper. Usually the tourists from the rich, developed part of the world go to the developing world to find what they cannot find in their own countries. Gay men have always been avid travellers and this is probably because they have always been searching for that elusive gay paradise where homosexuality will be free, and gay sex available unfettered. In 1894, for instance, Andre Gide found Oscar Wilde and Lord Alfred (Bosey) Douglas trolling in Algeria for sexual purposes.

North Africa has been a traditional happy hunting ground for sexual tourists because of the ambivalent attitudes and easy-going approach to gay sex. Joe Orton and his lover Kenneth Halliwell were frequent visitors to Morocco in the 1960s because of the easy availability of attractive boys.

In poor nations sexual favours can be bought very cheaply. American gay men have often use Puerto Rico and the

Philippines as a sexual tourist trap, while Europeans head for south-east Asia, particularly Thailand.

The Thai culture is very attractive for Western gays because it has no tradition of moralising about sex. Homosexuality is not considered in any way undesirable and is not condemned or treated differently.

Somerset Maugham noted a long time ago that "the Siamese were the only people on earth with an intelligent attitude about such matters."

Neither is there any stigma attached to prostitution – male or female. In the gay bars of Bangkok, the "off-boys" (a British term for rent-boys) can be found and taken home quite easily. Similar establishments in the suburbs are patronised almost entirely by locals. Some have, in fact, banned tourists from their premises because of their loud or anti-social behaviour. The Thai people do not generally like confrontational or impolite manners, and will recoil from rudeness or vulgarity. They will be reluctant to tell tourists that they are behaving badly, so it is as well to bear this in mind when having dealing with these gentle and graceful people.

Naturally those who are at a severe material disadvantage will greet well-heeled strangers enthusiastically. Having little to offer but their company and their bodies, the transaction is seen by some as unequal and exploitative. It is difficult to judge. I know many gay people in this country who are regular visitors to Thailand and who are entranced by the tenderness and availability of handsome young men. Both seem to benefit from the meeting, but moralists say that these young men would not entertain homosexual advances if they were not so poor.

Also, of course, if prostitution becomes a major source of income then standards inevitably deteriorate and corruption follows. Free-wheeling attitudes to sex tourists also almost invariably lead to the exploitation of children – much more easily available in poor countries than in the developed world. To deal with this, France has recently enacted a law which allows foreign countries to prosecute French citizens for child abuse committed abroad, even if they have returned home.

Within Europe, there are many destinations which are popular with gay tourists and where they go to have sex with each other rather than the natives. Gran Canaria is one, as is the Greek island of Mykonos and the Spanish resort of Sitges. In the USA there are several resorts in Florida (particularly Key West) that are popular with gay tourists as are Palm Beach and Russian River in California. Fire Island off New York has a long tradition of homosexual tourists and Provincetown, Massachusetts is also popular.

There are gay guides which give full information about which places are favoured at the moment, perhaps the most famous of these is the *Spartacus Guide* which tells not only about gay facilities but how the law stands in each country and what local attitudes you are likely to encounter.

Gay guide books can be purchased from:

- Gay Times Book Service, 283 Camden High Street, London NW1 7BX.
- Gay's the Word Bookshop 66 Marchmont Street, London WC1N 1AB (Tel: 0171 - 278 7654)

Tourism (2)

This is an expression describing heterosexuals who visit gay pubs and clubs as a sort of freak show entertainment (as an alternative, perhaps, to going to the zoo). Tourists at gay venues are generally resented and not well received. Sometimes they are hounded off the premises if their rubber-necking becomes too offensive.

Toys

There have always been sex toys, but manufacture and distribution of these items has improved considerably over recent years, so it is now possible to obtain the most sophisticated playthings quite easily.

Most popular with gay men is the vibrating dildo (which we've already described under that heading). The cock ring and the butt plug are also very common.

Butt plugs are solid, tapering pieces of rubber or plastic 6-7 inches long and about 4 inches round. They are intended to be stuck up the arse. They differ from vibrators in that they are intended simply to dilate the muscles of the anus, making it easier later to penetrate. Some people like to keep their butt plug in for extended periods, as they go about their business, on the basis that it helps them strengthen their anal sphincter. The real reason, though, is that it feels good.

Always ensure that the butt plug is well lubricated before you attempt to fit it, and wash it well (preferably in Milton or other non-bleach sterilising fluid) after use.

Another sex toy that is increasing in sophistication is the inflatable doll, which makes a reasonable substitute if wanking has become boring and a flesh and blood partner is not at hand. They are manufactured in both sexes, so you can get yourself a life-size plastic gentleman friend who will not complain whatever you do to him (short of sticking a pin in him, at which point his erection, along with the rest of his substance, will deflate). Of course, he won't be realistic, so you might have to make love to him the dark with your eyes shut and a peg over your nose to avoid the smell of burning rubber. However, if you've ever been tempted to undress an Action Man to see how complete his details are, an inflatable chappy might be of interest. He will usually have a vibrating willy, an ever-open and inviting mouth and some of the American ones even have anal openings. A recent report in a medical journal recounted the case of the plastic sex doll which had passed on syphilis. The object – the female version it was – belonged to a sea-faring chappy who abused his latex lady-friend and immediately passed her on to one of his ship-mates to similarly have his way. The owner of the dolly, however, was syphilitic and, after his session with the toy trollop, so was his friend. This is is an object lesson in safer sex. Keep your toys for your own use.

If you really want to splash out on this, there are available more substantial bendy-dolls, similar to the models used to teach mouth-to-mouth resuscitation in hospitals. These models have all kinds of refinements, like adjustable genitals, a voice that talks dirty if you squeeze him in the right place and quite realistic-feeling skin. These can cost anything up to £1,000, but it is unlikely that the manufacturers will offer a refund if he proves unsatisfactory or frigid.

Waterbeds, I suppose, can come under the heading of sex toys. They are custom-built rubber or plastic bags that are filled with water and then contained within a boxed surround. As you heave and hump aboard the mattress, the flow of the water inside will intensify the motion. It will either make you ecstatic or sea-sick.

Waterbeds usually have a special heater within them for cold weather. The plastic container for the water is usually divided into compartments so that if the bed is punctured your room will not be inundated with a flood of biblical proportions.

All the above items can be expensive and, because the manufacturers know that customers are unlikely to complain to the consumer protection agencies about their wares, they are frequently shoddily made. For those who do not wish to spend large amounts of money on unpredictable toys, there are alternatives. We've already considered some of the things that are laying around the house that can be improvised as sex toys (see Household Equipment). Here are a few more suggestions: hair dryers can be used to blow on nipples, knob-ends and other sensitive places. Electric toothbrushes vibrate and rotate nicely, but beware the bristles which might give a thrill in some instances, but might also be too scratchy. Don't clean your teeth with it after shoving it up your arse – get a separate brush-head for that!

TRANSSEXUALISM

Transsexuals (or gender dysphorics) often describe themselves as men trapped in women's bodies or women trapped in men's bodies. Unlike transvestites who have no desire to change their sex – only to experiment with dressing up as the opposite sex and seeing what it feels like to play that role – transsexuals actually want to become the opposite sex.

Transsexuals occur very rarely – about one in every 30,000 males and one in every 90,000 women.

Those male to female transsexuals who have decided to have their gender "surgically reassigned" are first given a course of hormones which help them develop secondary sexual characteristics, such as breasts, a higher voice and softer skin. After they have lived as a woman for several years, they can have surgery which involves the removal of their penis, testicles and scrotum and the creation of a neo-vagina. There may also be plastic surgery to enhance breasts and to soften features.

The word 'transsexual' was coined by Harry Benjamin in an article published in the *International Journal of Sexology* in 1953.

As many male to female transsexuals fathered children before they came to terms with their inner yearnings, it seems that sexuality doesn't seem to be a determining factor. I recently heard about a man who had changed sex and was now a lesbian woman. When you think about it, I suppose this is, statistically speaking, bound to occur from time to time.

Some psychotherapists think that transsexuals desire for surgery to change their sex is "intrinsically pathological" and should not be permitted, while others consider surgery should be available after long and careful evaluation.

Group to contact:

- Gender Dysphoria Trust
  BM Box 7624, London WC1N 3XX.
  Tel: 01323 - 641100.

Transvestism

Cross-dressing, gender-fucking, drag-wearing call it what you will, transvestism has many faces. For some gay men it is the opportunity to give real expression to those strong feminine impulses that lie within. For heterosexual men it seems to be a way of getting closer to the women they find so mysterious.

Agony columns regularly carry letters that says something like "I came home from shopping unexpectedly one day and found my husband dressing up in my silk lingerie. Is he gay?" The answer is no, he isn't. For reasons best known to themselves, some men actually feel closer to the women they love when they dress up in their wife or girlfriend's most intimate garments. Many a conventionally dressed businessman has been knocked down in the street and taken to hospital only to be revealed to be wearing Marks and Spencer's frilly knickers rather than Y-fronts. Nowadays there are even shops that specialise in "lingerie for men", and other companies that will provide all the facilities for men to fully explore their transvestism. For a price they will be loaned wigs, clothes and make up, and they will be able to socialise in full drag in sympathetic surroundings. For an afternoon, Jim can become Jennifer, and find out what it really feels like to be on the other side of the gender divide.

Gay men, on the other hand, like experimenting with drag because they want to know how it feels to be a woman who is wooed and courted by other men. Straight men find this alluring and repulsive in equal degrees. The British, in particular, are fascinated by cross-gender dressing, and drag queens have always been popular in this country's entertainment. From pantomime dames to Danny La Rue, from Old Mother Riley to Lily Savage and Dame Edna Everage, the Brits love men in frocks. Just so long as they stay up there on the stage and don't come down into real life. As soon as it stops being funny and starts being sexy, the Brits freak out over drag. There are few crimes more grave to the British male than a man in a frock who is being serious about it.

Group to contact:

- TV/TS Centre, 2-4 French Place, London E1. Tel: 0171 - 729 1466. There are regular socials and weekend events.

TRICKING

To 'turn a trick' is a slang term among American prostitutes (male and female) for servicing a client. Each client is 'a trick'.

TV STYLE

This is a sexual position which has nothing to do with transvestism. The participants do it doggy fashion so that both are able to watch television at the same time. OK if you want to watch porn while doing it, or maybe you don't want sex to cause you to miss the latest episode of Coronation Street.

Uniform

Uniforms are usually associated with active, thrusting young men and are therefore most attractive. The uniforms of the British armed forces are not particularly well-designed, though, and except for some of the combat gear, and the white trousers and red jackets of Guardsmen, they do little to excite erotic interest. Having said that, some of the younger able-seamen in their glowing white uniforms are irresistible.

The forces of other nations often seem to sport uniforms of breathtaking sexiness. The Israeli army is one particular favourite. Many of the Arab and African nations also allow their soldiers to wear trousers of indecently snug fit.

Other uniforms also have their fans. Policemen have a following, with suggestive truncheons hanging from their belts. The rozzers' following has increased since the TV show *The Bill* became so popular; I'm sure readers wouldn't mind accompanying some of those young constables on the beat. The same applies to firemen, especially since they are sometimes obliged to wear rubber trousers and boots – even gas masks – which appeal to some. Ambulance men, however admirable, I'm afraid, fail the uniform test.

Some young doctors, with their white coats flapping invitingly open, can send temperatures soaring, while peaked caps of all descriptions can certainly add an air of menace to an already handsome face.

The Californian Highway Patrol officers have also entered gay legend, with their motorcycle jackets, leather boots and mandatory shades. This get-up features frequently in the work of Tom of Finland.

I am also partial to the security guards in Marks and Spencer, whose brown uniforms are made of a sort of crimplene material, beautifully cut around the arse. Check them out next time you're buying a Chicken Kiev. The M&S personnel department certainly has good taste.

Perhaps the most appealing uniform of all is that of the Australian Lifeguard. You couldn't ask for anything more satisfactory than those tiny, tight trunks, which they drag up their arse so as to expose both cheeks. The nature of their job ensures that their bodies are always worth looking at, and even those ludicrous little rubber bonnets they're obliged to wear start to seem sexy.

Underwear

We've covered most individual items of underwear under the appropriate headings. Because our knickers, or straps or thongs, spend so much time in contact with the family jewels, they have become prized possessions to some. There is, indeed, a market for used underwear – especially if it is thought to have been worn by a hunk. If it is soiled by fluids that have leaked from his cock, so much the better.

These items change hands, sometimes for extravagant sums, and are used as masturbation aids.

Magazine to subscribe to:

- 'Spurt' especially for fans of underwear. You can obtain details from New Horizons, PO Box 54, Manchester M60 7AB.

Under arm sex

The armpits are extremely sensitive (note that this is the place most people get tickled), and so have become much used in sexual encounters. Because there are many sweat glands under the arm, it becomes very smelly. When the sweat is fresh (as after a work out) it can be a most exciting aroma, but its appeal soon fades as it becomes stale and B.O.-ish. Some people like to lick up fresh underarm sweat from their lovers, relishing the salty taste.

And, of course, fucking under the arm is a wonderful safer sex alternative. Clamp the arm close to the body and you have created a sensuous sex organ for both parties to enjoy. The person who is having their armpit fucked can alter the pressure to create new sensations. And you don't need to wear a condom (unless there are cuts and abrasions).

Underwater sex

Swimming, because it usually involves little or no clothing, has become eroticised. Indeed, the term "swimmer's body" is now used in gay personal ads to indicate a particular build – slim and strong, but not overly muscled.

Skinny-dipping – or nude bathing – is sensual in its own right, but if the circumstances are favourable it often leads to aquatic hank-panky. Most people have fantasised about having submerged sex, and so midnight dips in hotel swimming pools are sometimes accompanied by a quick, furtive shag. If you have a swimming pool of your own, then obviously more time can be taken over it, and more elaborate positions tried. The extra support that the water affords can create pleasing new sensations. Trying to do it in the sea, though, can be frustrating as the constant motion makes it difficult to concentrate, and the salty water makes oral contact unpleasant.

Why not do a Deborah Kerr and Burt Lancaster, laying at the edge of the tideline, letting the waves wash over you? This glamorous activity is not advised at Cleethorpes or Margate. For one thing it's so cold you'd probably need a winkle-picker to find the necessary equipment and secondly, both places have large populations of straight old age pensioners who sit in bus shelters, armed with binoculars, looking out for people who might be having sex-fun in order to report them to the police.

Jacuzzis, those swirling baths, are also popular places for getting your end away. With the bubbles hitting all kinds of tender spots, it can be a tremendously erotic experience. Most of us, though, have to make do with the ordinary domestic bath as our one opportunity to fuck under water. (see Bathroom)

Urethritis

Also known as N.S.U. (non-specific urethritis), it bears a superficial resemblance to gonorrhoea. It is a little-understood but fairly common sexually transmitted disease and can be difficult to get rid of once you've acquired it. It seems capable of lying dormant and then flaring up from time to time. Although it's not dangerous in the way that syphilis and gonorrhoea are, NSU should be treated because it can be extremely painful.

Urination (erotic)

See under Golden Showers and Water sports.

Vacuum Cleaner

Looking for a variation on wanking? Thinking about trying the vacuum cleaner as a sort of pseudo-suck? Forget it! There have been some nasty accidents to people who have shoved their dick into the Hoover. The nearer it gets to the body of the machine, the nearer it gets to the fan which creates the vacuum in the first place – and the nearer it is to disaster. Besides which, the vacuum a Hoover creates is far too strong for the purpose you require.

There are, for those who search them out, alternatives. One, which is a modification of the automatic milking machine used in the dairy industry, has had good reports. Then there is the hand operated vacuum pump which is quite widely available. If *Which?* ever does a consumer report on sex toys,

I'm afraid this one would get the thumbs down. It doesn't work as a wanking machine and it certainly doesn't make your cock bigger, as it claims.

You'd think with the advance of science, someone would have come up with something that was reasonably priced and was a bit more realistic. If they need volunteers for their R&D programme, I'm available.

Vampires are back in fashion – and a good thing too. Everybody knows that vampires are sexy and that Dracula is really an erotic fantasy. All that nibbling of the neck and sucking of blood. In the original Bram Stoker book, one of the Count's first victims is Jonathan Harker, a nice-looking young man who foolishly goes along to Transylvania to stay at Dracula's castle. The way that the Count treats him, and the lascivious way he plans to have him at the first opportunity, one can only assume that Dracula was bisexual and didn't mind who he sucked as long as he was sucking somebody.

Perhaps the sexiest of the screen vampires was Chris Sarandon in *Fright Night,* a blood-sucker you'd just (un)die for. The new crop of vampire pics are much more direct in their portrayal of the sexy aspects of the undead, although sticking the wooden stake in might still have some symbolic allusion.

Books to read:

- *Dracula* by Bram Stoker
- *Conversation with a Vampire* - Anne Rice

Vanilla is the flavour most associated with safeness and blandness; after all, who wants vanilla ice cream when they can have tutti-frutti? That once-innocent flavouring-pod has now become a cipher for anything boring, including sex.

Practitioners of S&M would say that their sex is Double Dark Chocolate Chip with Espresso Sauce compared to the Vanilla-esque activities of "straight" gays with their boring old wanking and sucking.

The problem is that there is so much pressure these days to participate in activities that many of us still secretly consider "way out", it seems almost inconceivable that anyone would admit that they don't like the more extreme expressions of sexuality and prefer nice, gentle vanilla sex. But if you find S&M a turn-off, and the prospect of group sex makes you want to vomit, don't be afraid to say so. Wild sex is not mandatory!

I'll just split the difference – I'm not vanilla and I'm not hot fudge sundae. I'll go as far as raspberry ripple.

V.D. CLINIC

This is where you go to have your sexual health checked. If you suspect you may have acquired a sexually transmitted disease, pop along to the special clinic (or department of genito-urinary medicine, or VD clinic) at your local hospital. Unlike other hospital departments, you don't need to be referred by a GP, you can just turn up. If you don't know where the local clap clinic is situated, ring up the hospital switchboard and ask, or look it up under Venereal Disease, in your local telephone directory.

VD clinics in this country are renowned for their discretion and respect for confidentiality. There is no need whatever to feel you are going to encounter moralising or judgmental attitudes. It would be very difficult for them to work effectively if this were the approach.

VERE STREET SCANDAL

A large-scale gay scandal erupted in London in 1810, and became known as the Vere Street Scandal because the notorious White Swan Tavern was situated in that street. The infamous hostelry was furnished for the amusement of the "sodomites" of the time. One room was kitted out with four double beds, another was made up as a lady's dressing room, a third was the "chapel" where "weddings" took place, sometimes between a six foot tall grenadier who played the wife and his "little master" who was much shorter. These "weddings" followed the full traditions, with bridesmaids and best men, and then a "wedding night" in which four couples would spend the night having sex in the large bedroom, in full sight of each other.

The upper part of the house was for "boys" who entertained casual visitors. Most of these boys had given themselves feminine names like 'Kitty Cambric' and 'Miss Sabina' (the former was a coal merchant and the latter a messenger at the local police station). Miss Sabina had two sons who also worked in the brothel. According to a pamphlet of the time, which described the whole set-up in lascivious detail, both were extremely handsome, and just as depraved as their father.

"Kitty" was particularly adept at sucking off, and his skill in this department brought customers from far and wide who had heard about him by...er...word of mouth. Miss Sabina, on the other hand, was said to have had the prettiest and tightest arse in the whole of London. Judging by the number of men who passed through his heavenly portals, I don't know how long that reputation for tightness held true.

In July, 1810 the police raided the joint and arrested seven people who were sentenced to two or three years in prison and a spell in the pillory.

VIDEOS

The video cassette recorder has brought a whole new world of sex within reach of just about everyone. Pre-1980, it was necessary to have elaborate film projectors if you wanted to see a bit of naughty, nowadays you just slip the cassette into the VCR and voila! – hour after hour of how's-your-father, complete with fast forward, rapid reverse, freeze frame and slow motion options.

Video cameras are becoming progressively cheaper and easier to use these days, so you can make your own movies. Those who like to keep a record of their activities – or simply want to replay it in order to analyse and improve their performance (rather like footballers do), will see the video camera as a god-send. Instant gratification, and none of this entrusting the film to "discreet" processors who charge the earth. It would be nice to keep a video record of your hey-day and then be able to play it back to yourself when you're old and grey. 'Oh yes', you'll be able to say to your cronies at the Old Folks Home, 'I was quite a lad when I was younger – want to see the kind of tricks I used to get up to?'

Reminiscing about the three-way you had back in 1994 will make a nice change from the community singing.

Many video cameras have an "automatic" button which means that you can position it first, set it going and then star in the resulting feature. This takes away the need for a cameraman, of course.

Making your own videos can prompt you into a whole new set of experiences, but you should be aware that if any of your filmed sessions involve things outside the law (more than two men at a time, sado-masochism, etc.), you might find them being played in court one day, to your detriment. This is what happened in the scandalous Operation Spanner case. The men were all involved in consenting S&M, but took Polaroids and videos of their games, which were subsequently used against them by the prosecution. It isn't unknown for the courts to cite letters, photos, videos and even drawings.

But for sex which is approved by the law, don't hesitate to use your video camera as an adjunct to your sex life. Remember, if you can't afford to buy a camcorder outright, you can hire one for one or more days from most TV rental stores.

Hardcore videos are, of course, completely illegal in the United Kingdom unless they got past the censor under the guise of "sex education", the definition of which seems to fluctuate wildly. Most police take great pleasure in searching the houses of gay men until they uncover the goods. A friend of mine was recently raided, and his house was searched, with his collection of 180 videos taken away. He knew that it was not illegal simply to possess the videos (selling, distributing, copying, importing or sending through the post are illegal, and so are any videos featuring children). My friend told the police that he had been given the videos by an acquaintance who had subsequently emigrated to Australia. He said they had been handed to him in a railway station.

There was no kiddie-porn among the 180 and despite threats and menaces, the police actually returned the videos because there was no law under which they could retain them.

If your collection is raided, and evidence is found of any of the things listed above (the first thing they look for is a second VCR which could be used for duplication), they will confiscate the videos and possibly prosecute you. But not all police forces behave in the same way.

- Legal erotic gay videos can be obtained from: Pride Video, PO Box 19, Pinner, Middlesex HA5 2U.

VIOLENCE

Violence and sex are often associated in the minds of those who seek to censor what we see, read and hear. "Too much sex and violence on the television" intones the ghastly Mrs Whitehouse. Well, I can assure her that if anyone has too much sex on the television it will make their back very sore!

But sometimes there *is* a connection between violence and sex. Rape is the most obvious example, and then sado-masochism. But even in loving, equal and consenting sexual encounters there can be an element of violence. Biting, wild thrusting, the holding down of arms and the sometimes rough invasion of our private areas all have elements of force about them, and they all can add excitement to the proceedings. More ritualised violence occurs between S&Mers.

The question is, when do gay men lose their virginity? Is it the first time they have sex with another man? Is it the first time they are penetrated by another man? Do they, in fact, ever lose their virginity at all given that the dictionary defines a virgin as someone who has never had "sexual intercourse" – presumably heterosexual intercourse?

Can you imagine it? Some of the dirtiest, most filthy sexual athletes on the gay scene may, in fact, still be virgins. Won't do much for their reputation, will it?

Men display virility in many ways: through their competitive spirit, through their courage (sometimes taken to foolish lengths), their machismo and their sexual aggression. Men are seen as "virile" if they can beat up their contemporaries, fuck their women stupid and generally behave like arseholes.

VIRUSES

Viruses have become the bane of our sex lives and we have to know all about them in order to ensure that as few as possible get into our bodies. Human Immunodeficiency Virus – which can lead to AIDS – is the one that must be avoided at all costs. Safer sex can help (see entry under that heading) and the use of condoms in all sexual situations in which HIV might be around.

Hepatitis is another nasty virus which can be transmitted sexually. We've dealt with Hepatitis B under that heading, but there is another version (Hepatitis A) which, while not quite so dangerous, is still very unpleasant. The chances of Hepatitis A proving fatal increase the older you are infected. If you contract this virus for the first time over the age of 49 your risk of dying from it is three in a hundred.

The good news is that a vaccine has now been developed for Hep A as well as Hep B. It is available on the National Health and a three-injection course will give ten years protection in most cases. Seven per cent of Britons carry A virus antibodies and they do not need the vaccination.

A French word meaning 'one who looks'. The relatively easy access we have to pornography these days has made voyeurs of us all. Watching other people have sex is almost as old as sex itself and, happily, there seem to be plenty of people around who get a kick out of being watched. As long as everyone's happy, I don't see the harm, although, of course, our stupid laws state that no more than two people may be together when homosexual sex takes place. I'm sure every one of you observes that law to the letter. (See also Exhibitionism).

Wanking

Masturbating is also called jerking off, tossing off, a hand job and beating the meat. Cockneys, with their rhyming slang, might say they have had a 'J. Arthur' (Rank) or a 'Barclays' (bank) or a 'Ham' (shank).

Whatever you care to call it, it is the most practised sexual act in the world, if not the universe. Research by Project Sigma (*Sex, Gay Men and Aids*, Falmer Press, 1993) showed that ninety-nine and a half per cent of gay men have masturbated to orgasm at some time in their life. The same research showed that in the month preceding the survey, 90 per cent of respondents admitted that they had wanked, on average 17 times each. Masters and Johnson maintained that it produces more intense orgasms than intercourse.

Most of us start wanking at a very early age. It doesn't take long to discover that nice sensations can be gained from playing around "down there", and it also doesn't take long to get your hand smacked if you do it in front of your parents.

From the moment that we realise privacy and privates go together we seek out secret places for our fun and games. That is, unless you are at an all-boys school, in which case it soon becomes apparent that everybody's doing it, doing it, doing it (and doing it again). In one school I heard about, there were so-called "milk races" in which several boys would compete to see who could be first to shoot a load. There was also a game called "biscuit". Here a piece of bread or a biscuit is placed on the table. Everyone then starts wanking over it. The last one to ejaculate on to the biscuit has to eat it – spunk and all!

An excellent description of the childhood discovery of wanking as a pleasant pastime, (and subsequent realisation that other people disapprove of it) is contained in the book *This Small Cloud* by Harry Daley.

Daley spent his childhood before the First World war in Lowestoft, where he was the son of a fisherman. Later he went on to become a most unconventional London policeman, with a propensity for East End rough trade.

"(The other boy) took out his large cock, the first I'd seen with hair around it, spat in his hand, and started to masturbate in the proper manner. After a minute or two he said he was tired and asked me to do it for him, which I did with pleasure.

Thus began one of the happiest periods of my life; the real beginning of my happy life; the first awakening to the knowledge of the pleasure and warmth in other people's bodies and affections; the realisation that physical contact consolidates and increases the pleasure and happiness to be got from mutual affection. It was all open and uncomplicated. We were not shy amongst ourselves. Whenever in our wanderings we came to a secret place, a wood, a shed or a deserted building, we would merrily wank away. Some boys were independent; others gave, or expected to receive mild affection.

Nowadays for some reason or other, this traditional experience is thought to be undesirable...We continued happily and unworried for a long time, until the sort of people one finds on the fringes of church life, noticing the dark rings under our eyes, warned us that boys who played with themselves went mad and had to be locked away. This was a typical mean, dirty-minded trick, for they had been boys themselves and knew it was not true. In any case they didn't stop us. Henceforth we wanked and worried, whereas formerly we had experienced nothing but satisfaction and contentment."

Despite its widespread appeal, wanking still has the reputation of being an activity confined to people who can't get "real" sex. However open boys might be about their masturbatory activities at school, it is unlikely that when they are adults they'd admit to wanking. "Wanker" is the worst insult (after "poof") that can be directed at a man. After all, none of the great macho heroes of popular culture ever stopped for the occasional hand job, did they? Can you imagine Mad Max, Superman, James Bond or The Terminator whipping out their chopper for a quickie? No, they always seem to have the 'real thing' on tap.

Truman Capote once said: "The great advantage of masturbation is that you don't have to dress up for it" while Woody Allen thought it the perfect kind of sex, because it is always with the one you love most.

Masturbation also allows full reign to the imagination. Fantasy comes into its own as part of the jerking off process. There is no pretence of love or affection with solo sex, it is simply self-gratification, and therefore it can be disassociated from any ethical code the wanker might otherwise adhere to. With wank-fantasies you can dream whatever you like in good conscience – it can be steamy, perverted, violent, crazy and just plain filthy – who will know except you?

Most men find that the most satisfactory way to wank is to take the shaft of the penis into the hand and pull the member back and forth, sometimes varying the rhythm of the strokes – faster and slower. Other techniques involve rubbing it against soft and warm objects, rolling it between the palms of both hands, gently squeezing the frenum and some people can actually force it between their legs and rub it between their thighs. Watching yourself doing it in a mirror is also popular (and an excellent educational exercise as it also makes you more familiar with your body's other secret places, like the arsehole, which aren't readily visible).

As human beings are blessed with two hands, the unoccupied one can be utilised for extra titillation: pinching and rubbing the nipples, fingering the arse, rubbing oil on the chest, manipulating vibrators, turning over pages of dirty magazines, running the video forward to more interesting sections of the tape – all these tasks can be performed without interrupting the flow of the pleasant pumping from the other hand.

Because of the strange, hypocritical and, one has to say, almost superstitious attitudes which hold sway in relation to this common pastime, wanking has acquired an incredible mythology. This was summed up for me in a cartoon I saw. A man with a white stick, dark glasses and a guide dog is saying: "The great thing about being blind is masturbation can't do you any harm."

From the moment it was decided that wanking was undesirable (see the Bible for full particulars) there grew up a thousand reasons why it "wasn't good" for a young man to beat his meat. Among the reasons: madness, blindness, growing hair on the palm of the hand, sterility, impotence and bad teeth. In 1776 the Swiss doctor, Tissot, wrote a pamphlet entitled "The heinous sin of self pollution and the frightful consequences of this abominable practice." In it he claimed that sperm was produced in the head and, therefore, masturbation reduced the size of the brain. Unfortunately, in 1778, the Pope took all this seriously and ordered the daft doctor to Rome, where His Holiness was persuaded that masturbation was causing the epidemic of typhoid that was sweeping through Italy at the time. This proves that Popes throughout history, even up to the present date, have been sexual ignoramuses and barmpots. The Pontiff then decreed that anyone found masturbating was to be beaten in the streets. Pope Pius XII declared that sexual self-gratification is "intrinsically and seriously disruptive", but a manual for Catholic youth, published in 1994 says that it could be harmless. It all depends on the type of masturbation and who is practising it. If it is practised as a "means of understanding and becoming close to the opposite sex" it is not a sin, If, however, it is "an assertion. of egotism" it becomes *vizietto* – a minor vice, though still not a sin.

In Islam, masturbation is generally condemned as it involves touching the "unclean" genitals. Men in some Islamic countries get round this prohibition by using elaborate non-manual methods of masturbating which involve melons.

In Victorian times a whole array of horrible deterrents were invented (see Infibulation) and scalding of the genitals became very popular - except with those on the receiving end.

In 1909 two doctors produced a book called *What Every Boy Should Know* and in it they included the following advice, which damaged several generations that followed:

"Whenever unnatural emissions are produced...the body becomes 'slack'. A boy will not feel so vigorous and springy; he will be more easily tired; he will not have so good 'an eye' for games. He will probably look pale and pasty, and he is lucky if he escapes indigestion and getting his bowels confined, both of which will probably give him spots and pimples on his face. The effects of self-abuse on a boy's character always tend to weaken it, and, in fact, to make him more untrustworthy, unreliable and probably even dishonest."

Until as late as 1940 a candidate could be rejected at the United States Naval Academy if it were discovered that he masturbated. Despite the efforts of people like Alfred Kinsey to demystify and rehabilitate wanking, the idea still persists that the practice is somehow dangerous or threatening. In his massive research into sex, Kinsey was not surprised to find that most men masturbate and he even reached the conclusion that not only was masturbation harmless, it was positively beneficial. He wrote:

"The record does include thousands of cases of boys living in continual conflict, oftentimes disturbed over the effects of such behaviour (masturbation) on their ultimate sexual capacities, occasionally attempting suicide – as a result of the teachings concerning masturbation. For the boys who have not been too disturbed physically, masturbation has, however, provided a regular sexual outlet which has alleviated nervous tensions; and the record is clear in many cases that these boys have on the whole lived more balanced lives than the boys who have been restrained in their sexual activities."

Everyone discovers their own favourite way of masturbating. The glory of it is that you can find the touch that is just right for you and the kind of manipulation that gives you most pleasure. There are lots of positions to choose from. In *The Gay Book of Lists*, author Leigh W. Routledge says that the seven most popular positions for masturbation are:

- Lying on the back;
- Standing Up;
- Legs thrown over the head;
- On the belly, fucking fist;
- On the belly rubbing against sheets, pillows etc.;
- On one's knees;
- On the toilet.

In his excellent book *Men and Sex* (HarperCollins), Dr. Bernard Zilbergeld encourages his readers to wank without guilt. He says that you do not have to think of reasons why you want to wank ("I can't find a partner" or "I'm not getting enough *real* sex"). Just do it because you want to and because it's pleasant. He then goes on to say:

"Now that we've said you don't need a reason for masturbating, we'd like to turn around and give you some reasons. Masturbation, done systematically and in accordance with a few simple rules, has definite therapeutic benefits. You can use it to learn more about your body and its requirements, and acquire skills useful in sex with a partner. We have found masturbation exercises very helpful in developing ejaculatory control and in dealing with erection problems. And you can learn a lot about yourself with these exercises even if you do not have a specific problem and are primarily interested in enhancing your sex life."

You can buy a copy of the book or get it from the library if you want to try Dr Zilbergeld's exercises.

There is no "normal" way to wank and no "correct" frequency of activity. If you do it when the fancy takes you – even if that's three, four, or five times a day – it's OK. Your body will tell you when you've had enough – you just won't be able to get a hard on.

Other than that, it's all hands on dick.

See also Zinc.

WATERSPORTS

As well as wind surfing, swimming and diving we can also include under this heading the non-Olympic event of pissing on each other for sexual pleasure. We've already explored this in some detail under Golden Showers

WARTS (GENITAL)

Warts are caused by human papilloma viruses. There are many different types of wart virus and each prefers a different part of the body. Venereal and genital warts grow on and around the penis and anus.

The foreskin, though, is the favoured place for genital warts to flourish. They pass from person to person through skin contact. Sometimes those who have warts in hidden places (inside the rectum, for instance) don't even know they're there, but if they are discovered, it is important to get them treated as soon as possible. In some instances they can turn cancerous.

A recent Canadian study showed that the virus that causes genital warts can survive for quite a long time in underwear, so it is as well not to share intimate garments with anyone.

The good news is that genital warts can be treated. If you have them, or suspect you might have them, visit the local special clinic who will be able to advise you of the best course of treatment in your particular case. They may be burned off with an ointment or a new technique can freeze them off.

Another essential item for S&M, whips come in all kinds of shapes and sizes. The strength of their application will depend on the tastes of the people using them, and mostly their application in 'scenes' is only symbolic, causing very mild pain. However, as part of a fantasy costume they can look very threatening (dressed up as a mediaeval 'flogger' for instance, complete with leather mask).

Some whips come complete with a smooth handle, which can be used as a dildo to violate the slave when the master feels like it. Some have multiple "tails", such as the tawse, which was originally invented to chastise naughty children and, of course, the cat o'nine tails, a much more serious instrument of punishment.

WILDE, Oscar

No dictionary of gay sex could be complete without mention of Oscar Wilde, perhaps the most famous homosexual of all time. Oscar, of course, would have preferred to have been remembered as one of Britain's great writers, which indeed he was, but his literary reputation was struck a deadly blow by the hypocrisy and anti-gay hysteria of Victorian England.

Wilde was the toast of the town following the hit productions of his glittering comedies *Lady Windermere's Fan* and *The Importance of Being Earnest*. His ready wit and a seemingly infallible way with aphorisms (see any dictionary of quotations for extensive examples) made him the darling of the glitterati and journalists, who hung on to his every word.

Society may have been at his feet, but Oscar had other needs which required young men to get down on their knees.

One of these was Lord Alfred Douglas, (the notorious "Bosey"), son of the certifiably loony Lord Queensberry (he of the rules of boxing). Queensberry was appalled that his son was having a relationship with Wilde and publicly challenged the great author about it on several occasions. Eventually he left a calling card at Wilde's gentleman's club saying that Oscar was "posing as a somdomite" (sic).

Wilde decided that he now had enough evidence to sue Lord Queensberry for libel and, in 1895, he did. But the prosecution proved to be a sorry mistake. The accusation was true – Wilde was indeed a 'somdomite' – and eventually he was put on trial. Homosexuality was completely illegal at the time, having recently been legislated against in parliament by the Labouchere amendment.

A parade of rentboys and blackmailers were produced at the trials to give evidence against Oscar and eventually – after a retrial – he was found guilty and sentenced to three years hard labour.

In one fell swoop, to satisfy the ranting evil of the homophobes of the day, one of the greatest writers in the English language was brought low. After serving every single day of his sentence, Wilde moved to France where he lived in poverty until his death, at 46, three years later. He wrote little of note in France.

Even at the end Wilde was still at it (uttering hilarious aphorisms, that is). In the sordid room of the Paris hotel where he was dying, he said: "This wallpaper is dreadful. Either it goes or I do."

Unfortunately for the world of letters, the wallpaper stayed.

Twenty-five years later, Laurence Housman wrote that the destruction of Oscar Wilde had served a purpose: "His downfall did at least this great service to humanity, that – by the sheer force of notoriety – it made the 'unmentionable' mentionable." But Richard Davenport-Hines thought: "His ruin was a triumph of extremism, which left a heritage of extremism."

Oscar was buried in Pere Lachaise cemetery in eastern Paris. His many friends and admirers subscribed to have his remains marked by an elegant monolith designed by Jacob Epstein. This has become something of a gay shrine, and carved upon the stone (at the rear) is a moving message which is pertinent to gay people everywhere.

The Pere Lachaise cemetery is enormous, but maps showing the location of the celebrities (including Edith Piaf) can be obtained from the attendants.

WOMEN

As sex surveys proliferate, one of the most interesting findings to emerge is that more than a few men who define themselves as gay also have sex with women from time to time. (Project Sigma found that more than half of the men who identified themselves as gay in their survey had had sex with women, and just over 4 per cent had had sex with a woman in the preceding month).

Why is this? Could it be that they are still trying to fulfil the expectations of those around them to be straight? Are they giving in to the pressure to do "the right thing"? Is it that they simply fancy a bit of something different from time to time? Or is the theory that we are all potentially bisexual true after all. There is no shortage of men on the gay scene who say they're straight but still aren't averse to the occasional bit of cock, just for the thrill of it. So why shouldn't it work the other way round?

Project Sigma put it this way: "We not only have to recognise the possibility of the existence of bisexual men who are attracted to and sexually active with both males and females, but we have to recognise that some 'heterosexual' men have sex with other men, and that being gay doesn't necessarily mean you never have sexual contact with women."

That other great sex researcher, Alfred Kinsey, wrote:

"Males do not represent two discrete populations, heterosexual and homosexual. The world is not divided into sheep and goats. Not all things are black and white. Only human beings invent categories and try to force facts into separate pigeon-holes. The living world is a continuum in each and every one of its aspects. The sooner we learn this concerning human sexual behaviour, the sooner we shall reach a sound understanding of the realities of sex."

There is less physiological difference between men and women than we imagine. Men have a vestigial womb – called the *utriculus masculinus* – which is situated in the prostate gland. Women have a corresponding prostate gland in their urethra and the clitoris is the equivalent of a penis. All the same, I think I'll stick with the fully-fledged variety.
See also Bisexuality; Homosexual and Heterosexual.

Working out at the gym has become something of an obsession for may gay men; they know that having a good body will get them more sex, but after a while the reasoning changes. Getting and keeping a sculpted, perfect physique becomes the motivation rather than the lure. This is how Chippendale Charles Walheim described the process: "The better your body becomes, the more insecure you become. It's a mind game you play with yourself, like chasing shadows. If you're constantly being appreciated for your looks, what starts off as an ego trip can soon become an insecurity trip. If I go out there thinking I haven't trained enough, I haven't eaten right, it can be tough. You compare yourself to others."

That philosophy of competition has now all but taken over the commercial gay scene in this country. Our pubs and clubs have become hotbeds of bimboism, with hordes of undeniably beautiful young males posing and primping in various states of undress. But their beauty does not always render them attractive. After you've had their bodies is there anything else? Do we now have to cruise in thought-free zones, where hard muscles and youth are the only thing that matter?

And are we setting ourselves up for psychological problems like bulimia and anorexia as the quest for the "perfect shape" takes over our lives?

Wrestling has an obvious homo-erotic appeal – two scantily-clad men rolling around in intimate contact, contorting themselves into ever more exotic positions, straddling each other, holding their legs over their heads and so on.

Professional wrestlers manage not to make it very sexy, but amateur wrestlers, who do it in the privacy of their own bedrooms, aren't quite so subtle. To start with they generally dispense with the trunks (just to make it authentic, as in the Olympic Games of ancient Greece, of course). Then the bodily contact revolves not around the shoulders and legs, but in the area between the waist and the knees.

"Wrestling" (as opposed to wrestling) has been used for centuries as an excuse for men to get close to each other and be erotic without actually admitting they're having sex.

The famous nude "wrestling" scene in D. H. Lawrence's book "Women in Love" was excellently brought to the screen in Ken Russell's film version, when Oliver Reed in his pre-repulsive days rolled unclothed on the fireside carpet with Alan ('Master') Bates.

Do you have a "straight" friend who keeps giving off signals of interest, but then pulling back when you try to take it further? You could always challenge him to a "wrestling" match and see what happens when you rip his shorts off.

- Alternative Wrestlers Europe – for gay fans of wrestling - write for info to A.L.T. Sports, PO Box 437, Glasgow G42 8HU.

X-Rated

Why "X" should have been chosen as the letter that represents the forbidden and the sexual, I don't know. Since the days when the British Board of Film Censors rated movies "U" (Universal), "A" (Adult), and "X" (don't ask me – explicit, perhaps?), the letter has had a certain mystique. Now if something is advertised as XXX, you can be sure that it has a strong sexual content. If it's advertised as XXXX it's probably an Australian lager.

YAK FACTOR

According to a survey of 550 teenagers in Minneapolis and St Paul, the "yak factor" – or talking to your partner – is an essential element in avoiding venereal diseases. People who were prepared to discuss their previous partners, Aids, condom use and other intimate matters, were three times less likely to have had a sexually transmitted disease.

Dr. Michael Resnick, who led the study for the National Institute of Child Health said: "Talking implies that you look before you leap."

The message is clear – conversation can save your life. Talk, talk and talk some more. And if you find it difficult to talk openly about sex, then have a bit of a practice to see which kind of sexual language you feel most comfortable with. There are several to choose from – the medical, the vulgar or the poetic. Which trips most easily from your tongue – is it "penis" or "cock"? "Testicles" or "bollocks"? "Oral sex" or "blow job"? "Fucking" or "making love"? "Shagging" or "sleeping together"? Say them out loud, and the words that make you cringe the least are the ones you should use when talking with your partner(s).

Yakkity, yak – it's an important part of sex.

YOUTH

Youth, the time of life when we most want sex and when we are least able to cope with the implications. Wouldn't it be nice if we got younger as the years progressed instead of older, so that we were at our most sexual – and our most beautiful – when we knew what to do about it. Instead, we have all that vigour and all that smooth skin and all the emotional immaturity that goes with it.

Youth, as the saying goes, is wasted on the young, but I don't think there are many young people who would agree. It can be torment finding out the hard way about sex and love and the whole damn thing, but it is an exquisite pain that those who've moved on would give their right arm to have again.

There are some experiences that you can only enjoy once in life, and losing your virginity is one of them. So make the most of it because it is likely to happen to you when you're young, and before you understand the full implications of the event.

The age of consent is, of course, a consideration; for heterosexuals it is 16, and for homosexual men it is 18 – although if the strength of campaigning around this issue is anything to go by it will soon be equal. Anyway, very few gay men wait until the official age before embarking upon their sex life, to expect them to is ludicrous. Project Sigma found that the average age for first homosexual experience was at just over 15.

It also turns out that the idea that young people are 'seduced' into homosexuality by older men is just another dirty-minded straight fantasy. The vast majority of young gay men have their first experience with someone within two years of their own age. Maybe one day in the not too distant future our lords and masters will accept that an eighteen year old (or a sixteen year old come to that) has as much right to choose who he will love as who he will vote for or who he will shoot in a war.

Group to contact:

- Lesbian & Gay Youth Movement, (for under-26s) BM/GYM, London WC1N 3XX. Tel: 0181 - 317 9690.

Y-fronts – those old-time underpants – had a reputation for being a turn-off. They had become associated with boring, old or overweight men. But, of course, anything that comes into intimate contact with cock cannot remain uneroticised for long. Y-fronts are back!

Naturally it all depends on what you put in them as to how sexy they are, but nowadays young men sport Y-fronts unashamedly.

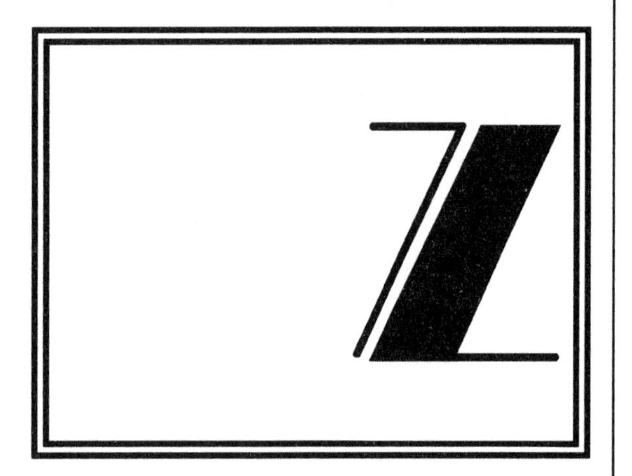

ZINA

Is a Muslim category which covers all forbidden sex. Religion – who needs it?

ZINC

Every time a man ejaculates he loses a small amount of zinc from his body. If you are having a lot of sex, it is important that this essential mineral is replaced. You can do it with a pill, of course, but it's always better to do it naturally, and choosing foods that are high in zinc is helpful. Such foods are steak, lamb chops, brazil nuts and egg yolks, as well as almonds, sardines, chicken and tuna.

Zinc tablets from:

- Holland and Barrett Health Food Stores. Branches nationwide. Consult your local phone book for the nearest. Most other health food stores would also be able to supply.

ZIP INJURY

The invention of the zip-fastener may have been a giant leap forward for mankind, but it is not without its perils. Anyone who, for any reason, does not wear underpants, puts the old chopper at risk every time they zip their fly. Getting the foreskin caught up in the zip mechanism is a fairly common reason for visiting the accident and emergency department.

I remember one very embarrassing incident when I was younger. I was staying at my grandmother's house. I returned home one evening after she had gone to bed and began undressing. Unfortunately, the skin of my cock got caught up in the zip. I wanted to scream out, but was mortified at the prospect of explaining the nature of my agony, and so somehow I kept silent. At that moment my grandmother called out from her room: "Did you have a nice time, dear?"

With tears of agony rolling down my cheeks I replied, in a perfectly ordinary tone of voice, "Yes, fine thanks, Gran." (Isn't it amazing what superhuman control we can exercise in order to save embarrassment?)

Then started the effort to extricate myself from this terrible predicament. I carefully rolled the zip back down, and the mechanism released the skin from its grip. I could have jumped for joy. No blush-inducing visit to the hospital would be required, no tittering nurses to face, no concerned relatives wanting to inspect the damage. But if that's what was needed to save the day, then that's what I would have done.

If hospital treatment is required, the usual approach is to sedate the victim then reduce the sensitivity of the penis with a generous amount of anaesthetic ointment. If necessary the zip is cut away from the trousers to manipulate it away from the skin without causing further injury.

You can see why some men still prefer button flies.

ZIPPER

Injuries apart, the zipper might be compared to the gateway to paradise. The sound of a zipper being lowered can, I imagine, be rather like the creak of the gate of heaven: if you enter either you will find St Peter waiting for you.

Zipper is also the name of a splendid magazine featuring photographs of large and gorgeous men. It has a long-established gay sex shop associated with it – one of the oldest in London.

Where to shop for gay essentials:

- Zipper Store, 283 Camden High Street, London NW1 7BX.

ZODIAC

If you believe that the stars have an influence on the way we develop, then you might be interested in an 'Astrosex' survey conducted by Mystic Meg, resident astrologer on the *News of the World*. Madame Meg received 25,000 replies from readers to her questionnaire about their sex lives and their Sun signs. She discovered that 5 per cent of Aires and Leo men liked to make love with both sexes, as did Leo women. Signs with the strongest preference for their own sex were Scorpio men (8 per cent), and Pisces men (7 per cent). Whether this information will be of any consequence when sizing up possible partners is dubious, but it is included for the sake of completeness.